Mathematical Snapshots

H. STEINHAUS

Mathematical

Snapshots

NEW YORK
OXFORD UNIVERSITY PRESS

18002

THIS book is an enlarged edition of my *Mathematical Snapshots*. It differs from the first version, which is now out of print, not only in the number of illustrations (three for each two of the former edition) but also in the insertion of a few pages containing mathematical reasoning of a very elementary kind. The chief purpose of *Snapshots,* to visualize mathematics, has been maintained throughout the new version, but the author hopes to be forgiven for occasionally strolling from his path when some interesting things demand verbal explanations.

The principle of avoiding appeals to statements and definitions hidden many pages back has also been retained; it enables the reader to skip over pages in which he is not interested. The anaglyphs of the first edition have been replaced by photographs. The questions addressed to the reader are sometimes easy to answer; sometimes the author does not know the answer himself. In some instances theorems are stated for which no proofs are known; it is for the reader to refute or to prove them. Sources of the figures and some comment on the text will be found in the Notes, pages 255-66.

I should like to thank Professors H. S. M. Coxeter and Herbert Robbins for their help in pointing out errors in the manuscript and in reading the proofs.

It would be impossible to make such a book without the patient and devoted help of photographers, modelers, and designers. To the names mentioned in the first edition I must add those of Messrs. B. Kupiec, R. Nowakowski, W. Wdowiak, and A. Trojanowski; their merits are exhibited on almost every page of the book.

Last but not least, let me express my gratitude to Mr. Philip Vaudrin of the Oxford University Press in New York, who encouraged me during my stay in the United States to repeat my former experiments with things as difficult to define as they are thrilling to look at, and which may be called mathematical objects.

H. Steinhaus

Wrocław, 3 March 1948

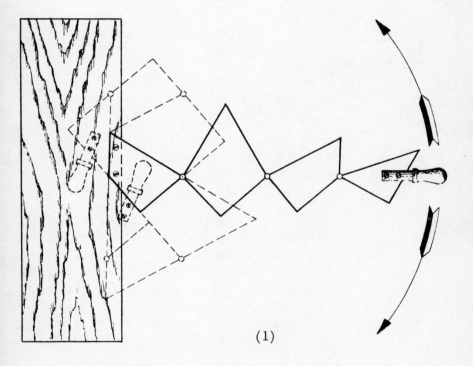

(1)

FROM these four small boards (1) we can compose a square or an equilateral triangle, according as we turn the handle up or down. To decompose a square into two squares we

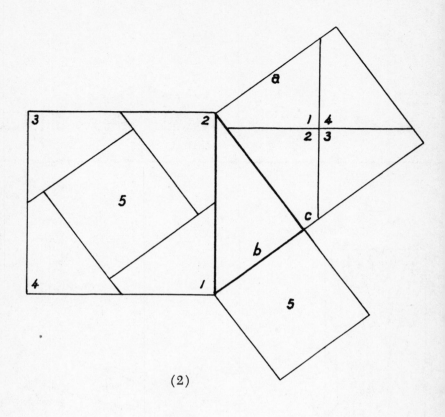

(2)

draw a right triangle (2); to verify that the
large square is the sum of the two others, we
cut the medium square into four parts by a
vertical and a horizontal line through its
center, and shift these parts (without turning them) to cover the corners of the large
square; the uncovered part of the large
square is exactly the size of the small square.

To verify this we have only to remark that $a = b + c$. The meaning of the theorem thus proved is clear when we look at the triangle 3, 4, 5 (3) : $9 + 16 = 25$. Thus we can draw a right angle by using a string 12 inches long with knots 3, 4, and 5 inches apart.

(3)

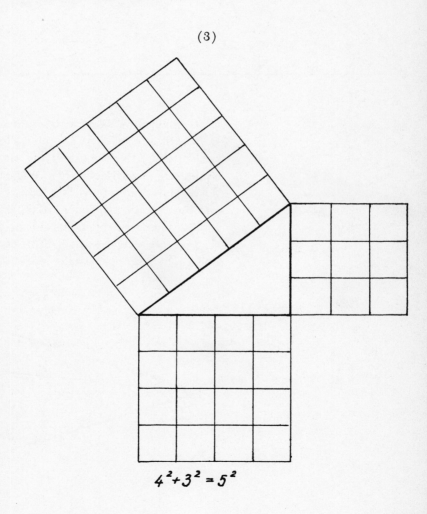

$4^2 + 3^2 = 5^2$

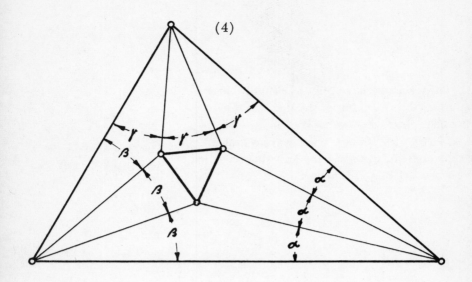

(4)

To draw an equilateral triangle we can start with any triangle (4) and trisect its angles: the little triangle in the middle is equilateral. The trisection of an angle can be done very accurately by first halving it (5) and then dividing the chord of the half into three equal parts: the radius cutting 2/3 off the chord trisects the angle. This construction is only an approximate one.

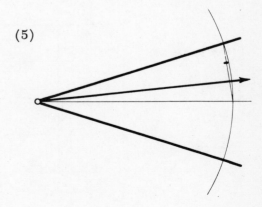

(5)

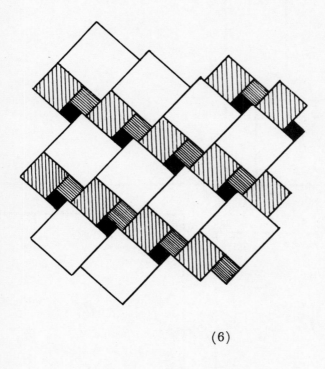

(6)

It is easy to cover a plane with squares of different sizes (6). A most interesting problem is presented by dividing a rectangle into squares, each of them different. On the following page they are given (7), nine in number, with sides 1,4,7,8,9,10,14,15,18. *Problem*: form a rectangle of them. This is the simplest example of division of a rectangle into different squares. A division into fewer than nine different squares is impossible.

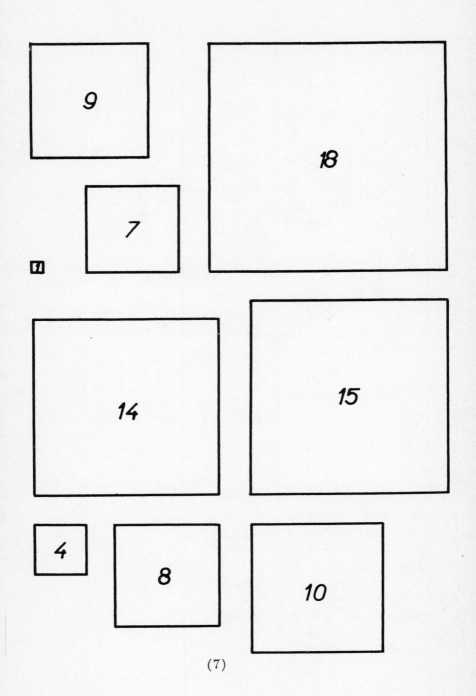

(7)

6

It is possible to divide a square into different squares. One of the simplest cases is drawn here (8). The sides of the 26 different squares are: 1,5,7,11,20,27,34,41,42, 43,44,61,85,95,108,113,118,123,136,168,172, 183,194,205,209,231. It is possible to solve the problem with 24 squares; how?

(8)

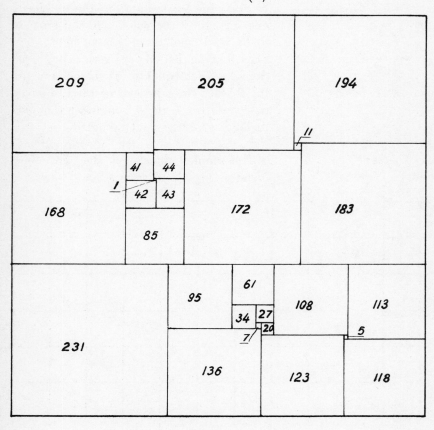

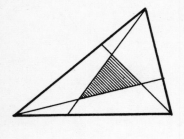

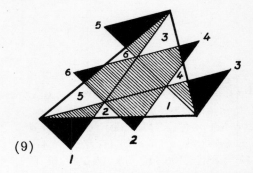

(9)

To cut out of any triangle another with an area equal to one-seventh of the whole, we divide (9) every side in the ratio 1:2 and connect the points of division with opposite vertices; the shaded area in the middle is one seventh of the whole and the proof is to be read from the adjoining figure: the black and the shaded parts give 7 congruent triangles, each equal to the shaded area; as the 6 black triangles can be used to cover the white parts, the 7 congruent triangles together give the great triangle.

The simplest division of the plane, into equal squares (10), gives a board for many

(10)

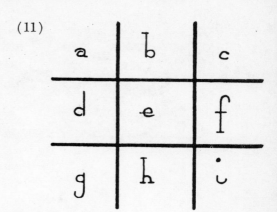

games. Two people can play 'Three-in-a-row' on this (11) nine-square chessboard. One of the players has three white pieces, the other has three black ones. They place the pieces in turn, and when all six pieces are on the board, each may be moved to any adjoining square (but not diagonally). The one who first places his pieces in a horizontal, vertical, or diagonal row is the winner. The first player is sure to win if he at once occupies the center square and then plays sensibly. For, if White occupies e, Black can counter in only two ways: by covering either a corner square or a side square between corners. If Black covers a, White ought to cover h, compelling Black to choose b, then White will have to cover c, causing Black to occupy g. Now White in the next two moves will pass from e to f and from h to i and win. If Black begins by choosing b, White will cover g, Black c, White a, Black d, and White will pass from g to h and then from h to i, moves that the black piece covering c will be unable to prevent. If the leader is not allowed to cover e, the game, if played cleverly by both partners, will end in a draw.

(12)

There are positions in chess that permit of an exact analysis. For example, the end-game of Dr. J. Berger (12) assures victory to White, provided White begins with the move *Q—QKt8*. White will lose if he begins with any other move, provided Black defends himself sensibly. But if White begins with the above-mentioned move and continues properly, in eight moves the game should become an evident win for him. Certain end-games are famous because of their cleverly hidden solution. For instance, it is by no means an easy task to find out how in the following situation (13) White can checkmate in four moves at most.

Dr. K. Ebersz's end-game is of an entirely mathematical character (14). It can be

(13)

(14)

proved rigorously that White will not allow Black's king to take any of his pawns, provided that he always moves to the square indicated by the same letter as the square on which Black's king is then standing. He must therefore start by the move *B-F*. If he observes this rule, the game will end in a draw, but if he makes one false move, then Black can prevent him, if he chooses, from applying such tactics, and may break through *X-Y* or *O-O*. An interesting endgame would be one in which the moves of one player were exactly determined by those of his opponent, the game also ending in a draw, but the player who first departed from the rule would lose the game, provided his opponent played in a certain way that would also be fully determined.

There is no mathematical theory of the game of chess, but there is one in certain simpler games. For example, in a box (15) there are 15 numbered tablets, and there is an empty space for one more. Lay the tablets in the box in any desired order (16)

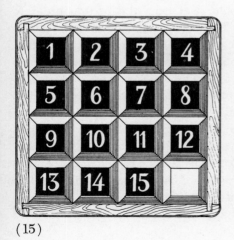

(15)   (16)

and then, by suitable moves, arrange them as they were originally ordered. The theory is as follows: let us call the vacant place '16'; then every arrangement of the tablets is a permutation of the numbers 1, 2, 3 . . . , 15, 16. Now, by writing these numbers first in their natural order 1 . . . 16 and then appropriately interchanging them with their neighbors, every desired order can be obtained. For instance, to get the arrangement 2, 1, 3, 4 . . . 16 one interchange is needed. We call it a move. Some arrangements require an odd, some an even number of moves. If an arrangement is to be reached by an odd number of moves, it is impossible to get it by an even number of moves. Let us imagine the contrary: an arrangement produced by an even number of moves and the same arrangement produced by an odd number of moves. Starting with the natural arrangement, executing the even number of moves and then the odd number of moves but in the opposite direction, we should come back to the natural order. Thus in an odd number of moves we could pass from the natural order to itself. This is impossible because the moves carrying any tablet away from its natural rank must be canceled by opposite moves. Thus the number of moves shifting any given tablet is even and so is the sum. Thus we can classify all arrangements into two classes: the 'even' and the 'odd' arrangements. Let us consider the arrangements of tablets in the box as an arrangement of numbers, reading them down line by line. When we shift the tablets in the box, we can only interchange the void place '16' with one of its neighbors. If this neighbor is the right or the left one, the interchanging is a 'move' in the previous sense, as if all the horizontal lines formed one line. If, however, we interchange the tablet '16' with its upper or lower neighbor, the step is equivalent to interchanging two tablets that, in the total line, have the distance 4. Such an interchange requires 7 moves, i.e. 7 interchangings of neighbors. To solve our problem, we must in any case bring the tablet '16' in the box back to its initial position in the bottom-right-hand corner; it must be therefore shifted as many times to the left as to the right and as many times up as down. The number of horizontal shiftings is therefore an even number $2h$, and the number of vertical shiftings also an even number $2v$. The whole process is thus equivalent to $2h$ moves plus $2v \times 7$ moves $= 2h + 14v$ moves and this number is even. Consequently, if an arrangement is to be obtained from the basic one by an odd number of 'moves,' the problem of returning back is insoluble. For instance, we cannot, by moving the tablets, change the arrangement given on our illustration into that shown on the drawing of the box, nor can we pass from the first to the second one. (Why?) All arrangements that can be reached by an even number of 'moves' define soluble problems; the reader may try to prove this statement. As soon as the theory was published in 1879, the pastime of the 'Fifteen Puzzle' went out of fashion.

All the games mentioned here and many others have something in common. Not only the end-games of chess but also 'wolves and sheep' and 'three-in-a-row' have theories indicating which of the colors (Black or White) will win, provided he plays properly. The theory teaches at the same time how to play properly. The case of draw seems to escape this statement but we can exclude it by the rule that the player who is confronted by a position that has previously occurred and who makes the same move a second time is defeated. Now, there is a general theorem to the effect that all games of the kind described above are unjust or vain. We call a game *vain* if it permits a draw when properly played by both partners. In certain games no draw is possible; we call them *categorical*. In others we can exclude the draw by supplementary rules, as mentioned above. Our thesis affirms that all categorical games are unjust. The meaning of this thesis is that only one color has a method to win, whatever his opponent may do. To discover this method may be very easy, as in 'wolves and sheep,' or very difficult, as in some endgames of chess; nevertheless the existence of the winning color and of the winning method is certain. The theorem is general enough to apply also to such games as chess, provided it has been made categorical by the rule of repetition mentioned above and by considering as defeated a partner who gets into a 'rut.'

To prove the theorem, consider an endgame that assures a victory to White after 4 moves at most. Let us call it an EG_4. It is clear that there exists an initial move for White so that whatever Black's answer may be, the resulting position becomes an EG_3.

Let us call this move a good one. White now has another good move, reducing the position to an EG_2, and so on, until an EG_1 is reached. Now there is a victorious move for White: the checkmate. Of course, a wrong defense by Black can accelerate his defeat; instead of being checkmated after exactly 4 moves he may be so after 3 moves. In any case White has a series of good moves leading to victory in 4 moves or less. Now it is clear what an EG_n means. All EG_n's where n is any natural number ($n=1, 2, 3 \ldots$) are called victorious for White. Let us consider the initial position in chess, when all 32 pieces are ordered ready for the battle. Two cases are logically possible and mutually exclusive: (i) the position is victorious for White, (ii) the position is not victorious for White. In the first case, the game of chess is essentially victorious for White: it is simply an EG_n. In the second case, the initial position is not an EG_n. In this case there exists for every definite move M of White an answer such that the resulting position is not an EG_n — in fact, if no such answer should exist, every answer would change the position into one victorious for White and, consequently, the initial position itself would be victorious for White, against our assumption. Thus we know that M can be answered by Black in a way that the resulting position is still not an EG_n. Applying the same argument to the new position, we see that Black can find an answer to any second movement M' of White's, leading to a 'not an EG_n.' As White can win only by getting an EG_1, — which never will happen,

	_1_	_11_	_111_	
_1_	1	3	2	
_11_	2	3	1	
_111_	3	1	4	

— and as the game is categorical, Black can win it, whatever White may do. We don't know which of the two cases, I or II, corresponds to the real modified chess, but we are sure that one and only one of them is true, a fact implying that chess is an unjust game. The same reasoning applies to checkers, halma, and many other games. If they are not categorical, they can be vain. We do not know whether ordinary (not modified) chess is vain or not. In the negative case we know that it is unjust, but we do not know which color is the privileged one. Even if we knew it, we should not necessarily have the knowledge of the winning method. If we knew that chess is vain, we could still be ignorant of the methods leading to a draw.

There are games of a different kind to which the theory advanced above does not apply. The same board used for the 'three-in-a-row' game can be used for the following one. The board (17) carries 9 numbers, some black and some white. White writes _0, 00_ , or _000_ on a piece of paper and

Black writes ɪ, ɪɪ, or ɪɪɪ on another. Then they produce the scraps and determine the column and the line on the board. The number found in the line and column gives the amount of dimes White has to get from his opponent, if it is white, and the amount he has to pay to Black, if it is black. The peculiarity of this game consists in its not being 'closed.' To explain the meaning of this remark, let us suppose that White always chooses 00 and that Black has already noticed this preference. The best Black can do under such circumstances is to choose ɪɪ; he will win three dimes by this method in every run. Of course White will learn this trick of Black by experience, and before long he will find that he has to change his habit and choose 0 . This policy will bring him two dimes in every run, so long as Black keeps to ɪɪ. It is easy to see that this mutual adaptation never leads to a rigid method for either of the partners. In chess the situation is different. In Dr. Berger's end-game the solution given in our text is the best for both partners. If White knows that his opponent never makes mistakes, he will begin with $Q-QKt8$; otherwise he could not expect a victory in his 13th move. If Black knows his opponent is an ideal player, he will answer by $B-QB5$; any different move would enable White to checkmate him before the 13th move. The contest will thus continue according to the 'principal solution' of our text. In such a play the two methods, Black's and White's, are mutually best. The existence of such 'principal solutions' makes a game 'closed.' Chess is thus a closed game, and all ordinary games like

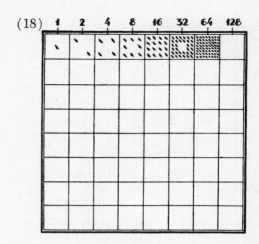

(18)

checkers, halma, and so on which we have shown to be unjust or vain are closed, whereas our new game of 9 squares is neither closed nor unjust; it is open and equitable like 'matching pennies.' Of course, the fact that in these games there is no first and no second player is essential.

There is a legend to the effect that the Brahmin who invented chess demanded of the King of Persia as a reward as much wheat as would cover the whole chessboard, beginning by placing one grain on the first square, two on the next, and so on, always doubling the number of grains (18). It turned out that not only the Shah but all the granaries in the world put together would be unable to furnish so much wheat. The Brahmin demanded in a modest way

$$1+2+2^2+ \ldots +2^{63}=2^{64}-1$$

grains. The number runs into 20 figures and has divisors. (What divisors?)

If we placed two chessboards alongside each other and took one grain from the last square of the second board, there would remain upon that square

$$2^{127} - 1 =$$

170141183460469231731687303715884105727

grains. This number has no divisors. It is the highest known *prime number*, i.e. indivisible by any smaller number (except by 1). Euclid has proved that there is an infinity of prime numbers, but up to the present we are unable to state any prime number greater than the number of 39 figures written above. The number $2^{257} - 1$ is composite; it has been proved to have divisors but they are not known.

(19)

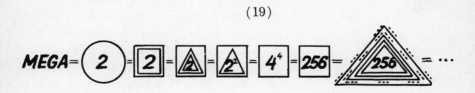

It is easy to write down very great numbers. Such giants can be defined very simply if we agree to write $\triangle{a}$ instead of a^a, $\boxed{a}$ instead of 'a in a triangles,' and $\bigcirc{a}$ instead of 'a in a squares.' Then the number 'Mega'= $\bigcirc{2}$ is already too great to have any physical meaning. We have (19), the last symbol being 256 in 256 triangles, and the reason why we have abandoned the ordinary system of writing numbers is clear. (The reader may try to explain the 'Megiston' given by $\bigcirc{10}$).

(20)   (21)

The chessboard has produced a great many puzzles and games. Thus we may place upon it eight queens (20) in such a way that none of them can attack any other. There are 92 different ways of so disposing the queens, all of which are obtainable from 12 fundamentally distinct arrangements, by suitable rotations and mirror reflections of the chessboard. It is possible to place five queens (21) on the chessboard so that each square will be attacked by at least one queen. There are 4860 solutions to this problem, and they may be obtained from 638 basically distinct ones. The problem may also be solved in such a way that the queens cannot attack each other. (How?)

Suppose some squares of the chessboard to be 'forbidden' to the king. They are chosen in such a manner as to prevent the king from reaching the right border of the chessboard if he starts anywhere on the left border. Then a rook can travel from the upper border to the lower one without leaving the forbidden squares. This property is shared by rectangular chessboards (with $m \times n$ squares); it is obvious but no simple proof is known to the author.

A knight may walk over the whole chessboard in 64 moves in such a way (22) that the polygon thus formed will have its center in the center of the chessboard, and the consecutive numbers of the squares will form a 'semi-magic square,' that is, their sum, in each column and in each row, will be equal ($=260$; no other sum is possible; why?).

The great mathematician Euler was interested in this 'knight's tour' and other similar problems, e.g. that of the '36 officers.' This last problem is as follows: How is a delegation of six regiments, each of which sends a colonel, a lieutenant-colonel, a major, a captain, a lieutenant, and a sublieutenant, to be placed so that neither in any row nor in any file will regiment or officers' rank be repeated? This problem is impossible but we shall easily place 25 officers in the desired order (23): the shades stand for regiments' colors and the letters for ranks.

(23)

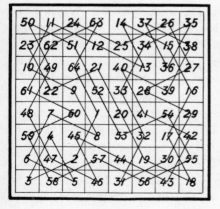

(22)

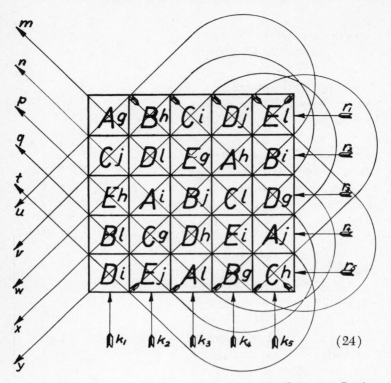

(24)

These so-called Graeco-Latin squares can be applied for practical purposes. To study the influence of different treatments on different varieties of a plant we can divide a field into 25 plots (24) and denote by capital letters A, B, C, D, E five different varieties; the small letters g, h, i, j, l represent five different fertilizers. The arrangement exhibits in 25 plots the 25 possible combinations of 5 varieties with 5 fertilizers. If the rows have different degrees of humidity, our arrangement shows the combination of all varieties with every degree of humidity. For instance, the lowest degree of humidity r_1 appears combined with A, B, C, D, and E, and the same is true of all degrees r_2, r_3, r_4, and r_5. Moreover, the humidity r_1, appears combined with all fertilizers and the same is true for all degrees. The columns correspond to different systems of cultivation: it is obvious that the first column k_1 appears combined with all varieties, with all fertilizers, and with all humidities; the same is true of any other column. We have two systems of diagonals: m, n, p, q, t and u, v, w, x, y. The first system corresponds to five different times of sowing, the second to five different times of reaping. Let us consider the diagonal m: it crosses every row, every column, its plots carry all the capital letters, all letters of the group $g-l$, and all letters of the system $u-y$. Thus, if we compute the average yield m of the five plots m, we can expect to have eliminated all influences of treatment and of variety except the influence of the date of sowing. If we compute the average yield A of the five plots designated by this letter, we have eliminated all influences except the influence of variety. These statements, which result immediately from the inspection of the Graeco-Latin square, lead to the following method: let M be the average yield per plot, i.e. the total yield divided by 25; let us designate, as above, by a letter the average yield of the plots corresponding to that letter, i.e. the sum of the five yields of the corresponding plots divided by 5. It is possible now to compute the following sum:

$$(M\text{-}A)^2 + (M\text{-}B)^2 + (M\text{-}C)^2 + (M\text{-}D)^2 + (M\text{-}E)^2$$

and analogous sums for other groups of letters:

$$(M\text{-}g)^2 + (M\text{-}h)^2 + (M\text{-}i)^2 + (M\text{-}j)^2 + (M\text{-}l)^2,$$
$$(M\text{-}r_1)^2 + (M\text{-}r_2)^2 + (M\text{-}r_3)^2 + (M\text{-}r_4)^2 + (M\text{-}r_5)^2$$

and so on.

The next step is to compare these sums. If, for instance, the first sum is greater than the second, we are entitled to the inference that the influence of the variety on the yield is greater than the influence of the fertilizer. The exact 'analysis of variance'—this is the name of the method—is, however, more sophisticated.

Rectangles, Numbers, and Tunes

LET us use the word *normal* for a rectangular sheet of paper that folded into two rectangular halves gives a sheet similar to the original one (25). Denoting its sides by a and b, we have the proportion $a : b = b : a/2$. Let us take two normal sheets and glue the base b of the second one to the long side a of the first (26). We get thus a great rectangle with sides $a+b$, b (the shaded part of the drawing) and a small rectangle with sides $b, a-b$ (the white part of the drawing). The proportion $a:b = b:a/2$ gives $a^2 = 2b^2$, which makes it easy to verify the proportion $a+b : b=b : a-b$. Thus the shaded rectangle is similar to the white one. Now the doubly shaded part is congruent to the white rectangle. Let us call the shape of the shaded rectangle hyper-normal; we have proved that by cutting off two squares of a hyper-normal sheet the remainder is still hyper-normal. Now let us suppose that we have a normal sheet with sides equal to a inches and b inches respectively, a and b being whole numbers. Of such a sheet we can make a hyper-normal one, as already seen; its sides will be whole numbers, when measured in inches: let us say p for the number of inches of the large and q for the number of inches of the small side. By cutting off two squares, we get a new hyper-normal sheet; its sides will be q and $p-2q$ inches respectively. It is evident that these numbers are integers and that the new long side is less than half of the old long side. Proceeding in this manner, we get smaller and smaller hyper-normal sheets; after p steps we still ought to have a sheet with sides expressed in whole numbers when measured in inches—which is absurd because we lose at least one inch at every step and the long side must eventually disappear. This fact

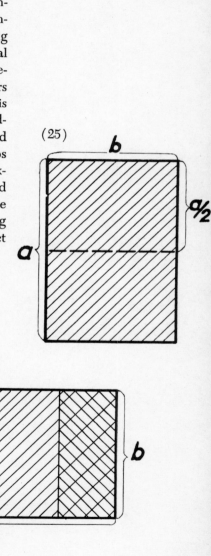

(25)

(26)

proves that there are no normal sheets with integer sides. It does not matter which units we choose: the argument holds for microns as well as for inches. The ratio of the sides of a normal sheet is $\sqrt{2}$, which means a number that multiplied with itself gives 2. What we have shown is that $\sqrt{2}$ is irrational, i.e. that it is not a ratio of two integers a/b.

(27)

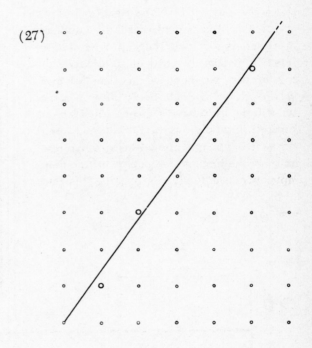

We can show our result on the 'lattice of integers' (27). This is simply an array of points in rows and files at equal intervals like hop-poles or like the vertices of the squares of a chessboard extending over the whole plane. Putting the corner of a normal sheet to cover the lower left corner of the lattice and drawing the diagonal of the sheet, we get the oblique straight line. When we look along this line, we see not one hop-pole. (Why?)

The number $\sqrt{2}$ may also be expressed thus:

$$1+\cfrac{1}{2+\cfrac{1}{2+\cfrac{1}{2.}}}$$

(Why?)

Hence approximate values of $\sqrt{2}$ are 1, 3/2, 7/5, 17/12 . . . The slope of the oblique line is $\sqrt{2}$; the fractions 1, 3/2 . . . give certain points of the lattice. For instance, 3/2 determines the point found by going 3 intervals up and 2 intervals to the right of the corner; we see these points approaching more and more closely the oblique line.

As we have shown already that $\sqrt{2}$ is not a ratio of two integers, a/b, we know that we cannot find integers a, b such as to have $a^2=2b^2$. In other words, given two equal detachments of soldiers forming two squares, it is impossible to make one square of them. However, it is possible to satisfy this whim if we do not care about one soldier more or less. The fractions already found give the following quadratic arrangements:

$$2^2+2^2=3^2-1, \; 5^2+5^2=7^2+1,$$
$$12^2+12^2=17^2-1 \ldots$$

To get all the fractions needed we can start with 1/1 : the sum $1+1=2$ gives the next denominator, the sum $1+2=3$ gives the numerator, $3+2=5$ is the third denominator, $2+5=7$ the third numerator, and so on. $\quad \frac{1}{1}\lfloor \; \frac{3}{2}\lfloor \; \frac{7}{5}\lfloor \; \frac{17}{12}\lfloor$

The arithmetical rule is as follows: if p/q is one fraction and P/Q the next, we have

$$Q = p+q, P = q+Q = p+2q.$$

Let us suppose that the fraction p/q gives a quadratic arrangement with one soldier more or less:

$$p^2 - 2q^2 = \pm 1;$$

we can easily show that P/Q is such an arrangement too. In fact, we have

$$P^2 - 2Q^2 = (p+2q)^2 - 2(p+q)^2 = p^2 + 4pq + 4q^2 - 2p^2 - 4pq - 2q^2 = 2q^2 - p^2 = \mp 1.$$

Now $1/1$ is obviously a solution ($1^2 - 2.1^2 = -1$); it follows that the next fraction is a solution too, and so on; all the fractions are solutions and yield quadratic arrangements. We have stated this fact previously, but now we have a proof.

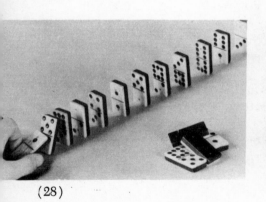

(28)

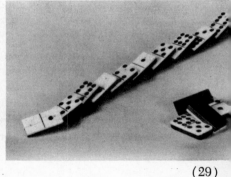

(29)

The method of our reasoning reminds us of playing with dominoes: (28) they are all standing in a file, and striking the first piece makes (29) all the other pieces fall. To foresee what will happen we have only to know that the first piece will be struck and that the pieces are standing so close that the fall of any piece implies the fall of the next piece. Such reasoning is called *mathematical induction*.

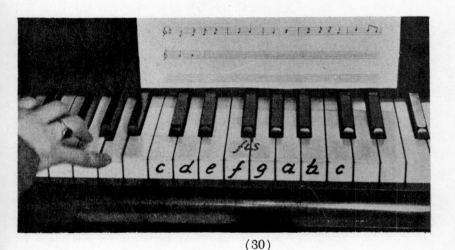

(30)

Rational and irrational numbers are connected with the problem of the musical scale (30). We call irrational those numbers that, like $\sqrt{2}$, are not expressible by a ratio a/b of two integers. In the scale 'C major' (31) the intervals C-D, D-E, F-G, G-A, A-B must be equal ('whole tone'),

(31)

while the intervals E-F and B-C are only a half of the former ones ('semitone'). The simplest concords have long since been examined on the monochord, and it has been found that the smaller the numbers expressing the relative frequency of the vibrations, the better the concord. High C has twice as many vibrations per second as low C, hence the octave is expressed by the ratio 2:1. The ratio 3:2 gives the fifth $(G:C)$, 4:3 the fourth $(F:C)$, 5:4 the major third $(E:C)$, 6:5 the minor third $(F:D)$. The distance C-C is equal to 12 semitones $=$ 4 minor thirds, so we ought to have

$$(6/5)^4 = 2;$$

but the fraction on the left side is 2.074, hence too great. This is not to be remedied, for it is impossible to attain a pitch such that all resulting concords have ratios expressible as ratios of whole numbers. Between F and G lies $F\#$ (the black key in the very center of the octave); the ratio between C and $F\#$ is the same as between $F\#$ and high C, amounting to an augmented fourth. If we call x the ratio $F\# : C$, we get $x.x = 2$, hence $x = \sqrt{2}$, which is an irrational number. The piano has a tempered scale; all the semitone intervals are equal to $^{12}\sqrt{2}$ but the concords are not exact. The violinist, following his musical sense, differs from the piano: for him the augmented fourth is 7:5 (he recedes from the tempered fourth just as does the point 7/5 on the lattice from the oblique straight line).

The infinite continued fraction giving $\sqrt{2}$ is not the simplest one; obviously

$$1 + \cfrac{1}{1 + \cfrac{1}{1 + \cfrac{1}{1.}}}$$

is the simplest possible. The number x given by this fraction is irrational. As we see be-

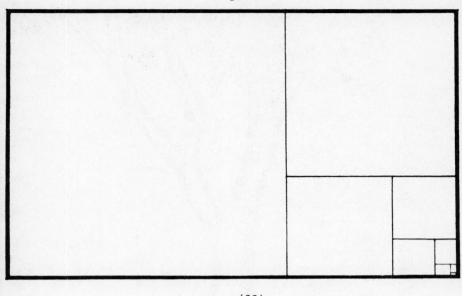

(32)

neath the first numerator 1 the fraction itself as denominator, we get

$$x = 1 + \frac{1}{x}, \quad x^2 - x = 1, \quad x = \frac{1}{2}(\sqrt{5}+1).$$

Let us use the name 'golden rectangle' for a
rectangular sheet that (32) is composed of
a square and a rectangle similar to the whole
sheet. If a and b are its sides, we get
$a:b = b : a-b, \quad a^2 - ab = b^2, \quad (a/b)^2 - (a/b) = 1.$
The fraction a/b satisfies the same equation
as x: it is therefore equal to $(\sqrt{5}+1)/2$.
This number being irrational there are no
integers a, b able to give a golden rectangle.
We can, however, proceed as with $\sqrt{2}$; by
terminating the continued fraction at various stages, we get successively

1/1, 2/1, 3/2, 5/3, 8/5, 13/8, . . .

These fractions approach more and more

31

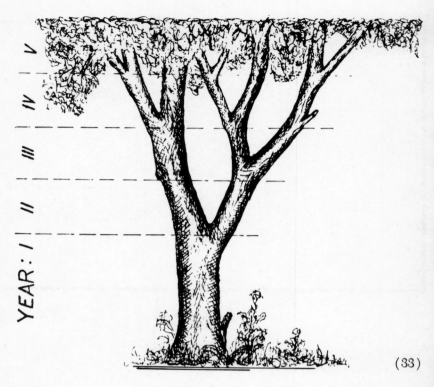

YEAR : I | II | III | IV | V

(33)

the true value of the golden ratio, which is 1.618 . . . The numerators 1, 2, 3, 5, 8, 13, 21 . . . are the so called Fibonacci numbers: we get them by successive addition, beginning with $1+1$:

$$1+1=2,\ 1+2=3,\ 2+3=5,$$
$$3+5=8,\ 5+8=13,\ \ldots$$

The nth number of the Fibonacci sequence is

$$\frac{1}{\sqrt{5}}\left\{\left(\frac{\sqrt{5}+1}{2}\right)^{n}-\left(\frac{-\sqrt{5}+1}{2}\right)^{n}\right\}$$

We could prove it by mathematical induction. How? If a tree (33) puts forth a new branch after one year, and always rests for a year, producing a new branch only in the following year, and if the same law applies

32

to each branch, then in the first year we should have only the trunk, in the second, two branches, in the third, three, then 5, 8, 13, etc., as in Fibonacci's sequence.

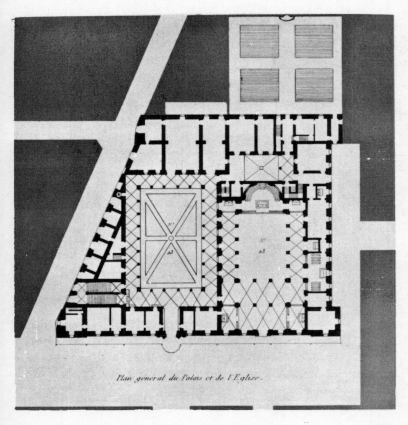

Plan général du Palais et de l'Eglise.

(34)

This courtyard's sides (34) approximately observe the 'golden ratio.' The golden division of a segment is such that the whole has the same ratio to the greater part as the greater part to the smaller one: both ratios are then golden. (Why?)

We can decompose the golden rectangle into an infinite number of squares, marking

(35)

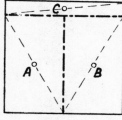

(36)

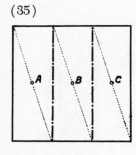

(37)

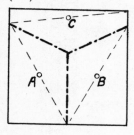

(38)

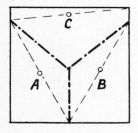

first the greatest square possible in the rectangle (Fig. 32), and proceeding similarly with the remaining rectangle, which is a golden rectangle too, and so on. This geometrical procedure leads, when translated into arithmetic, to the infinite continued fraction composed of unities, with which we started.

When there is a herd of cattle in a rectangular pasture and three cowboys have to watch it, they will probably first divide the square into three (35) equal rectangles and place themselves in the three centers, everybody being bound to watch only his rectangle. If, however, cowboy C is cleverer than his colleagues, he will persuade them to a new division (36) that assures to everybody the same maximum distance to cover in case of emergency. This distance is equal to half of the diagonal of the new rectangles and is the same for each cowboy; it is less than the maximum ride in the first division. The two cowboys A and B would realize after a certain time that their areas are greater than the area surveyed by C and would propose a new delimitation that (37) will neither change their positions nor affect the length of the maximum ride, but only satisfy the fair condition of every point being trusted to the man who is nearest to it. B, being dissatisfied with the new covenant because of the unequal distribution of the areas, which is still favorable to C, proposes an augmentation (38) of the area belonging to C, without changing the positions and the maximum rides. This plan having been accepted, A remarks that his principle of the nearest man has been violated. *C* replies that it can be saved if *A* and *B* change their positions (39) without changing the frontiers. This having been done, *A* and *B* discover that they are wronged, because their maximum ride is now longer than *C*'s. Finally they agree to resume the first division into equal rectangles.

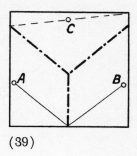

(39)

Weighing, Measuring, and Fair Division

WE need only four weights (40) to obtain every weight from 1 to 40, if we are allowed to place them on both arms of the scale. This corresponds to the development of numbers in the ternary system, taking 3 as the radix. All numbers from -40 to 40 (0 excepted) can be thus written as $\pm27\pm9$ $\pm3\pm1$, using one or more of the four numbers 1, 3, 9, 27. This solves the puzzle of the 'girls' names': We write down 80 different feminine names and give them numbers from -40 to 40. Four cards are signed *brunette, blonde, auburn,* and *red;* one side of card is labelled *black eyes,* the other *blue eyes.* We learn to read 'brunette' as 27, 'blonde' as 9, 'auburn' as 3, 'red' as 1, 'black' as *plus,* and 'blue' as *minus.* Now if, for instance, Mabel has the number -25, we have $-25 = -27$ $-1+3$ and thence the name Mabel must be written three times: on the card of brunettes on the blue side, on the card of the auburns on the blue side, and on the cards of reds on the black side. Someone who does not know the trick is given the cards and is told to think of a name and to find out the possible hues of hair and eyes. If he thinks of Mabel he will answer: She can be a brunette with blue eyes, an auburn with blue eyes, or a redhead with black eyes. The man with the catalogue of names computes mentally $-27 -1+3 = -25$ and finds the name Mabel.

When we have to compare objects on a scale without balance-weights, we can tell only which of the two is the heavier one.

(40)

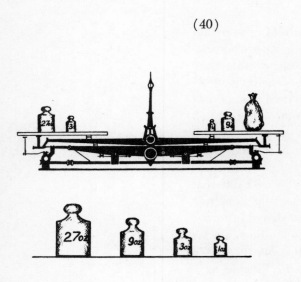

$1 = 1$	
$2 = 3 - 1$	
$3 = 3$	
$4 = 3 + 1$	
$5 = 9 - 3 - 1$	
$6 = 9 - 3$	
$7 = 9 - 3 + 1$	
$8 = 9 - 1$	
$9 = 9$	
$10 = 9 + 1$	
$11 = 9 + 3 - 1$	
$12 = 9 + 3$	
$13 = 9 + 3 + 1$	
$14 = 27 - 9 - 3 - 1$	
$15 = 27 - 9 - 3$	
$16 = 27 - 9 - 3 + 1$	
$17 = 27 - 9 + 1$	
$18 = 27 - 9 + 3 - 1$	
$19 = 27 - 9 + 1$	
$20 = 27 - 9 + 3 - 1$	
$21 = 27 - 9 + 3$	
$22 = 27 - 9 + 3 + 1$	
$23 = 27 - 3 - 1$	
$24 = 27 - 3$	
$25 = 27 - 3 + 1$	
$26 = 27 - 1$	
$27 = 27$	
$28 = 27 + 1$	
$29 = 27 + 3 - 1$	
$30 = 27 + 3$	
$31 = 27 + 3 + 1$	
$32 = 27 + 9 - 3 - 1$	
$33 = 27 + 9 - 3$	
$34 = 27 + 9 + 1 - 3$	
$35 = 27 + 9 - 1$	
$36 = 27 + 9$	
$37 = 27 + 9 + 1$	
$38 = 27 + 9 + 3 - 1$	
$39 = 27 + 9 + 3$	
$40 = 27 + 9 + 3 + 1$	

The question arises how to do it when we have more objects than two and we are allowed only to compare them pairwise. It is easy to find the heaviest one by comparing first a pair, then the heavier one with a third object, the heavier of the two with the fourth, and so on. For n objects we need thus $n-1$ steps. It is the same with tennis tournaments: to determine the best among n players, $n-1$ matches are sufficient. But they are necessary too. In fact, the best player has to be compared directly (by the result of a match) or indirectly (by the results of a chain of matches) with every other player. If we represent players as points and matches as lines joining the points, the winner must be connected with every other player by a system of lines and thus all the n points will be connected. Now it is easy to see (41) that we need at least $n-1$ lines to connect n points. We can prove that fact

(41)

by induction: we certainly need one line to connect two points; if we need $n-1$ lines to connect n points and we have to adjoin a $(n+1)$th point, the new point must certainly be connected by a new line to one of the old points and that step gives n lines as necessary. The tournaments are usually played by the cup method: players are grouped pairwise, the winners of the first round form new pairs—which gives the second round and so on until the final match

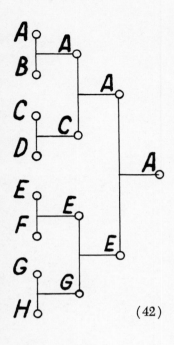

(42)

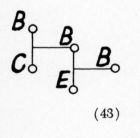

(43)

gives the decision. So, for instance, if we have (42) 8 players, there are 4 matches in the first round, 2 in the second, and 1 in the third round, 7 matches in all; it is impossible to diminish this number, as we have already proved. Now, there is a custom to give the second prize to the finalist, i.e. to the player who has lost in the last round. This system is obviously unjust, because this player has not been compared with the players B, C, E who were beaten only by the first-prize winner and thus were eliminated before the last round. The number of these players is 3 in a tournament of 8. An additional tournament, requiring two matches, (43) is necessary to determine the best of three. Generally, to determine the two best players among n contestants, $n-1+[\log_2(n-1)]$ matches are enough. It has been proved that no smaller number is generally sufficient. 'Generally' means here that no method of determining the two best players is available that works in all cases with a smaller number of matches than the number given above. The fact that it can happen by accident that A beats B, B beats C, C beats D, and son on, so that after $n-1$ matches we have determined not only the first- and second-best player but also the whole classification, $A, B, C \ldots N$ is not an argument for the chain method as described before, and against the cup method with an additional tournament; it shortens the procedure only because the players were listed by chance according to their ability.

To rank all objects by weighing them pairwise (and the same with ranking players by matches) we can adopt the following

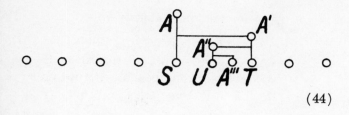

(44)

procedure: Let us suppose that we have already ranked a set of objects and we have to find a place among them for a new one. (44) We seek first the median, i.e. the object S which has as many objects above it as beneath it — if the number of objects is even, we call both objects in the middle of the range medians. Then we compare the new object A with the median; if it turns out to be heavier, we compare it with the median T of the upper half, if it is lighter, with the median of the lower half of the range, and so on, until it finds its place A''' between two neighbors U and T of the range. Let us begin with two objects: to rank them, one weighing is sufficient, to rank a third, two weighings at most are necessary; to place a fourth object among three already ranked, we compare it with the median—then, if it is heavier with the heaviest one and if lighter with the lightest one: that makes two steps. Thus we get the following sequence:

To place a new object among
   1, 2, 3, 4, 5, 6, 7 . . . already ranked objects
   1, 2, 2, 3, 3, 3, 3 . . . new weighings are

sufficient. Thus to rank
   1, 2, 3, 4, 5, 6, 7, 8, 9, 10, 11, 12, . . . objects
   0, 1, 3, 5, 8, 11, 14, 17, 21, 25, 29, 33, . . .
                    weighings are sufficient.

The formula for n objects is

$$1 + kn - 2^k, \text{ where } k = 1 + [\log_2 n].$$

It has not been proved that there is no shorter proceeding possible, but we rather think it to be true.

(45)

Our method of weighing reminds us of a problem of gunnery (45). There is a tank emplaced on a highway and the observer reports on which segment of the road it is situated. The gunner can hit any point of the segment he chooses, but the effect of the shot is reported to him by the observer only in terms of 'before' or 'beyond' the target. How should be proceed? If he shoots first to the midpoint of the segment, then to the midpoint of the first half if he was told 'beyond,' and to the midpoint of the second half if he was told 'before,' and continues to halve the segments, he will do best. The maximum distance between the target and the best shot among the n first shots is $L/2^n$, L being the length of the segment. This worst result happens only if the tank stands on one of the endpoints of the segment. The whole problem can be considered as a game. If the enemy knows the method of the gunner, he can place his tank so as to keep as far as possible from the n first shells. If this method is that of 'halving,' the enemy can do nothing better than to occupy one of the endpoints: this procedure gives him the margin of security $L/2^n$. Now let us see what happens if the gunner has chosen another method and his enemy has discovered it through spies or sagacity. The method will in any case result in a series of shots and this series will be the same in two experiments if the series of signals 'before' and 'beyond' is the same in both, because no other information is available for the gunner. Let us consider first $n=1$, that is to say a single shot. There is no method possible to reduce the error beneath $L/2$ by a single shot. Only one method can reduce it to $L/2$ in all cases: shooting at the midpoint. If this method is adopted, there is no better method to reduce the distance by a subsequent shot than the method of hitting the midpoint of the first or of the second half, conforming to the signals 'beyond' or 'before'; this reduces the error to at most $L/4$. If, however, the first shot was not a shot at the center, there is for the enemy — who knew it before the battle — a segment greater than $L/2$ in which to place his tank. We know already that this distance can be halved by the gunner in the next shot if he has the best method, but even in this case it will give more than $L/4$ for the maximum error. Thus we have proved that the popular method of halving is best for $n=2$. The same result follows for every n by induction. The classical method appears to be the best in the sense of the theory of games. We have not proved, however, that it is best in the sense of the theory of probability, i.e. that it reduces the expected distance to a minimum. Now, such a question requires knowledge of the probability of the tank's occupying any given place. The worst case for the gunner occurs when his enemy knows his method; in that case he will place his tank so as to secure the maximum margin of security. This argument reduces the new problem to the old one and we are justified in saying that in practice halving is the best method in the sense of probabilities too.

The ranking of weights is quite a different problem from that treated already, if we are allowed to put several of them at once on the scale. If we have eight coins of the same appearance and we know that one of them is false and weighs less than any of the seven true coins, we can find the false one by two weighings. We put three coins on each side of the scale and if one side rises, we compare two of the three coins: if they are equal, the remaining third is false; if one of them is lighter, it is the false one. If, however, the first weighing gives no difference of weights, we compare the two remaining coins to discover the false one. The problem is more complicated if we have thirteen coins, one of which differs in weight from the others, but we don't know whether it is heavier or lighter than the standard coins. Nevertheless, three weighings are sufficient to find the forged coin (46). The coins are marked by numbers 1—13. The first column of the drawing shows the first weighing; there are eight coins involved, four on each arm, and two cases are possible: difference of weight or equality of

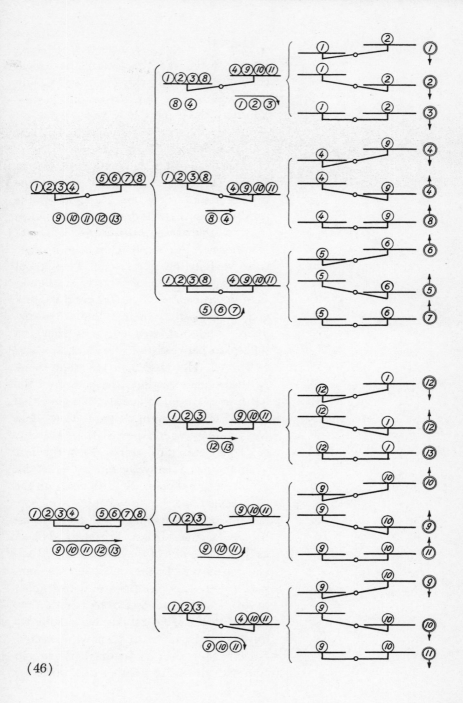

(46)

43

weight. In every case a second weighing follows, which is to be seen in the second column, and in every case the second weighing leads to three possible results: (i) the arm with three coins 1, 2, 3 of the first set sinks; (ii) it rises; (iii) remains in balance. We have now six results possible and each of them leads to a weighing of a pair of coins. The results are to be seen in the third column: there are 18 items in the third column and the false piece is shown in a double circle; the arrow indicates whether it is heavier or lighter. In a single case we find the forged coin 13, without learning whether it is heavier or lighter than the true coins. To understand the procedure let us study the first line of the diagram. The first weighing has shown a difference between the coins 1, 2, 3, 4 and 5, 6, 7, 8. The false coin is among them. In the second weighing the coin 4 on the left arm has been replaced by 8; nevertheless the left arm went down as in the first weighing: — which proves that 4 and 8 are equal and thus sound. Now the first weighing has already shown that 9, 10, 11, 12, 13 are good coins; thus all coins on the right arm in the second weighing are good, and, as there is inequality, it must be attributed to the left arm bearing 1, 2, 3, 8; as 8 is sound, one of the coins 1, 2, 3 is bad and too heavy. In the third step we compare 1 with 2 and see the arm with 1 going down, — which proves 1 to be bad and too heavy. In the same manner we get the results in all 18 cases. It is, however, interesting to study the case leading to the forged coin without saying whether it is too heavy or too light. The first weighing gives a balance between 1, 2, 3, 4 and 5, 6, 7, 8. The false coin is among 9, 10, 11, 12, 13; the horizontal arrow shows that we do not know if it is too heavy or too light. A second weighing shows equality of 1, 2, 3 and 9, 10, 11; these coins are sound, thus 12 or 13 is false. Comparing 12 with the sound 1, we get a balance in the third weighing, which proves 12 to be good and 13 to be bad; as 13 was not touched during the procedure, we do not know whether it is too light or too heavy.

It has been proved that n weighings are sufficient to find a bad coin among $(3^n-1)/2$ coins and that this number cannot be diminished. The meaning of this assertion has been explained already: although no method of guaranteeing less than n weighings exists, we can find by accident the false coin among 13 in two weighings. Four weighings are sufficient and necessary for 40 coins. The reader may find a false coin among four by two weighings (the case $n=2$).

Liquids are measured by vessels having a definite volume. If we have three vessels of respective volumes 12, 7, and 5 gallons and we have to divide 12 gallons of wine contained in the biggest vessel into equal parts, we can do it by using an appropriate billiard table (47) of rhomboid shape, the angles being 60° and 120°. We have to imagine the vessels lying on the plane of the table and the lines drawn from the billiard ball determining at every moment the levels of wine in the vessels. The

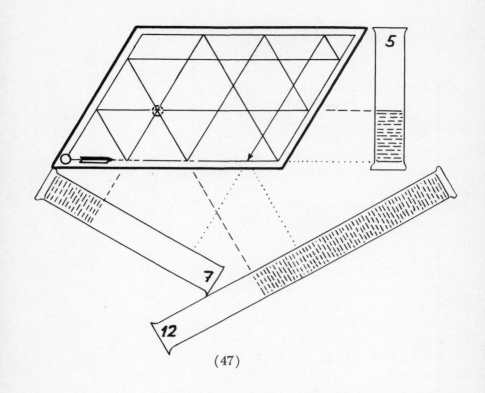

(47)

picture shows the path of the ball as a full line and every straight segment of this path corresponds to the act of pouring wine from one vessel into another. We see a path of 11 straight portions — thus 11 acts are sufficient; this is the simplest solution. When driving the ball initially along the short side of the billiard table, we get another solution. (How many steps?)

If we have a rectangular billiard table, the relation of whose sides (48A) can be expressed by whole numbers (e.g. 5:3), a ball hit from a corner at an angle of 45° will strike one of the corners after several rebounds (in this case six). The explanation is supplied by the illustration (48B), in which the broken course of the ball is replaced by a straight line. The rectangles represent the successive reflections of the billiard in the edges (as in mirrors). If $p:q$ is the ratio of the sides expressed in least integers, the ball rebounds $p+q-2$ times before reaching the corner. (Why?)

If we wish to hit ball B with ball A so that ball A will strike in succession the right, the lower, the left, and the upper edges, we must (49) find the reflected image B_1 of point B in the upper side, as in a mirror,

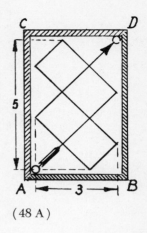

(48 A)

(48 B)

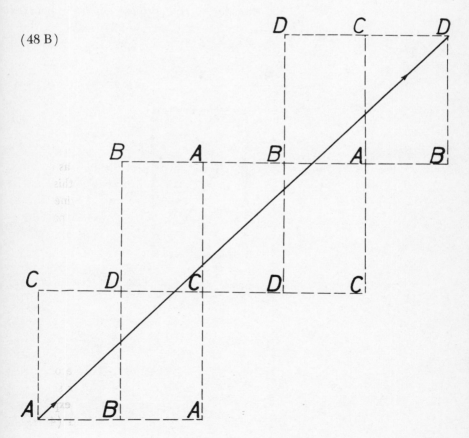

then the reflected image B_2 of point B_1 in the left edge, then the image B_3 of point B_2 in the lower, and the image B_4 of point B_3 in the right edge. Then we aim at B_4 with ball A. We can ascertain every possible method of hitting our mark by forming a rectangular lattice, as in sketch 48B, and placing in every rectangle the images B_1, B_2, B_3 . . . of point B. By joining A to one of these B_n, we obtain a straight line; to get the broken course we have only to fold the rectangles along the common edges, beginning with the last one; eventually they all cover the first rectangle and, if the paper is transparent, the broken course appears. This method can be verified also in the problem of hitting the corner.

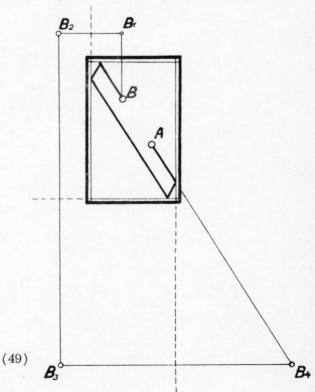

(49)

To divide an object like a cake into two equal parts, we can adopt the old custom of letting one partner cut and the other choose. The advantage of such a procedure is obvious: neither of the partners can object to this division. The first can secure the part due him by dividing the cake into two parts that he considers to be equally valuable; the second can secure at least his due part, by choosing the more valuable part or — if he considers them equally valuable — either part. It is presumed here that the object has the property of not losing its total value by division, i.e. that the values of the parts give by addition the value of the whole, this property being admitted by both partners, even if they disagree as to the valuation of the whole object and of its parts. There exist such objects: heaps of nuts, for instance. There arises the question of how to divide fairly an object into three or more parts. The answer is given by the following rules, which may be explained here in the case of five partners, the procedure being essentially the same for any number of partners. They may be called A, B, C, D, and E. A has the right to cut from the cake an arbitrary slice; B is free to diminish the slice cut off by A, but is not compelled to do it; in turn C has the right (but not the duty) to diminish the (already diminished or not diminished) slice, and so on. After E has made use of his right (or declined to do so), we see who was the last to touch the slice. Suppose it was D; Then D gets the slice, and the remainder of the cake (including the bits cut off) has to be divided fairly between A, B, C, and E. In the second round the same procedure reduces the number of partners to three, and the third round reduces it to two; the two partners divide the rest of the cake by the procedure initially explained: one cuts and the other chooses. Now let us see how every partner can secure his due part whatever his companions may do. If in the first round A cuts a slice that he considers to be 1/5 in value, it can happen that nobody touches it and A gets it; in this case he is not wronged. If, however, one or more of his companions diminish this slice, the man who was the last to touch it gets it and, as it is diminished, A must consider that more than 4/5 of the value is left to be divided equally among 4 partners, himself being one of them. In the second round A has to proceed as before: If he happens to be the first again, he has to cut a slice that he considers 1/4 in value of the remainder. This policy is not sufficient; we must show how a partner has to behave when he is not the first. Suppose that B considers the part cut by A to be too great, that is to say, greater in value in B's estimation than 1/5 of the whole. He has only to diminish it to the proper size; if he turns out to be the last diminisher, he gets it and is not wronged. If he fails to get it, it is because somebody else has touched the slice after it had already been diminished by B to a size considered by B as 1/5. One of these subsequent diminishers thus gets a slice that B considers to be of smaller value than 1/5, so that B comes to the next round as a shareholder of a remainder that he considers of greater value than 4/5 of the whole cake, the number of partners being now 4 and B one of them. Now the method is clear: if you are the first of n partners in any round, you have to cut off a slice that you consider to be $1/n$-th in value of the part before you, whether it be the whole or the remainder of the cake; if you are not the first in the given round and you see a slice cut by one of your companions, a slice greater, in your estimation, than $1/n$-th of the part, you have to diminish it to $1/n$-th; if it has been cut so that the slice is $1/n$-th or less, in your estimation, you have to keep off. This method insures everybody at least his due share.

If the cake is not to be divided equally but in a given proportion, for instance 2:2:3 among A, B, C, we can reduce the question to a division into 7 equal parts, letting A act as if he were 2 persons, similarly for B, and giving to C the rights of 3 persons. This procedure is very long; it is possible to shorten it as follows: C has to divide the whole into 7 parts; he is warned that he will get 3 of them with no right to choice or adjustments; if he can save his rights by dividing the cake into parts he considers equal in value, the procedure is therefore fair in respect to C. Now A and B have to examine the parts and tell which of them are 'good,' i.e. equal or greater than $1/7$, and which are 'bad,' i.e. less than $1/7$. In general the classification will be not the same for both examiners. Suppose that A has found 4 or more good pieces and B 4 or more good pieces. Then we can find 2 pieces designated as good by A and 2 other pieces designated as good by B; giving them respectively to A and B, we give to each of them a part of the whole considered by him as at least 2/7th of the whole; the remaining 3 parts go to C and the division is completed without any reasonable objections possible. There is another case: one of the partners A, B considers 4 or more pieces bad. Suppose it is A. Now B is allowed to choose among these pieces 2 that he considers good and he can get them without wronging A. As the remaining 5 pieces make more than 5/7 of the whole in A's estimation, B can find among them 2 that put together give more than 2/7 in his opinion; C gets then the remainder and the division is finished. It can happen, however, that B cannot find among the 4 pieces A considered bad 2 good pieces for himself; in this case he can find among them 3 pieces he considers bad. Now both A and B agree that these 3 pieces are bad and they can give them to C (who cannot object); as to the remainder they must both admit that its value is more than 4/7 of the whole. They form a block of this remainder and divide it fairly according to the rule: 'A cuts into 2 parts and B chooses his part.' Thus the fair division can be accomplished in all cases by $6+1=7$ cuts at most. It would be difficult to show that this division cannot be executed by less than 7 cuts.

There is a simpler method to divide fairly a building lot into equal parts. Suppose each of 3 men A, B, and C has a 1/3 share in a lot. The umpire orders A to divide the lot into 3 equal parts by two lines perpendicular to the street; B and C receive the same order. Now the lines are examined by

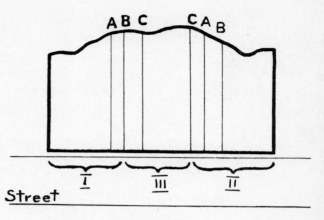

(50)

the umpire; the sketch (50) shows one of
the possible results. The umpire grants part
ɪ to A, part ɪɪ to B, and part ɪɪɪ to C, thus
giving to each more than 1/3 of the lot in
each person's own estimation. The sketch
answers the question only in one of the 8
essentially different possible cases. In some
of them the surplus for one of the partners
is zero. The advantage of this method is
that all shareholders are admitted simultaneously to the determination of the parts;
the role of the umpire is purely automatic.
The division could be carried out in such a
way that the provisory division lines remain
unknown to the partners who did not draw
them.

There is another problem of division en-
countered in economic life: the division of
indivisible objects like houses, domestic
animals, pieces of furniture, cars, and works
of art. If, for instance, an inheritance composed of a house, a mill, and a car has to
be divided among four inheritors A, B, C,
D participating in equal shares, this division
is generally made by a sworn appraiser who

determines the values of the objects so that the inheritors can choose the objects and, if they agree, in principle, satisfy by payments in cash the mutual claims arising from the differences in value.

This procedure has many inconveniences connected with the determination of the objective value of things by an official appraiser or by a court of justice. It is possible to make a fair division without appealing to them:

An umpire, who has to act only as a sort of automaton to keep records and make computations, summons the inheritors to write down their estimates of the objects. They are not supposed to discuss the matter among themselves but every one of them is allowed to be helped by friends and experienced persons. Thus a table of values is put down by the umpire:

	A	B	C	D
House	$6,000	$10,000	$7,000	$9,000
Mill	3,000	2,000	4,000	2,000
Car	1,500	1,200	1,000	1,000
Sum	10,500	13,200	12,000	12,000
Share	2,625	3,300	3,000	3,000
Value	1,500	10,000	4,000	0
Claim	1,125	−6,700	−1,000	3,000

In the above table each person's share is got by dividing his estimate of the total by 4. In every row the greatest item appears in a frame and the corresponding object is attributed to the person whose name stands above the column. Thus A gets the car, B the house, and C the mill. The values of the objects subtracted from the shares of the persons invested with them give the claims. A appears with a claim of $1,125, D with one of $3,000, whereas B has a negative claim of $6,700, and C a negative claim of $1,000. This means that B and C have to pay money to the umpire and A and D have to get money from him:

A $1,125	B $6,700	$7,700
D 3,000	C 1,000	−4,125
4,125	7,700	3,575:4 = $893.75

This computation shows that the payments will leave the umpire with a surplus of $3,575; divided by 4 this gives $893.75 for each inheritor. Thus
A will get the car and
$$\$1,125 + \$893.75 = \$2,018.75 \text{ cash}$$
B will get the house and will have to pay
$$\$6,700 - \$893.75 = \$5,806.25 \text{ off,}$$
C will get the mill and will have to pay
$$\$1,000 - \$893.75 = \quad \$106.25 \text{ off,}$$
D will get $3,000+$893.75 = $3,893.75 cash.

Thus everybody will finally get more than his due share of the inheritance, the value of the total and of the objects given to him being estimated according to his own valuation. For instance, A has a car and $2,018.75 in cash; as the car is worth $1,500 to him, he has a total of $3,518.75, whereas he had estimated his share at only $2,625. He has got $893.75 over his due part and the same is true of other partners. This method works with unequal shares too, and it can be modified so as to diminish the payments in cash. (How?) The 'fair division' gives the following game. A heap of different coins (51) are on a table inside a boundary, and the partners who have contributed equally to the heap have to divide it among themselves after the manner of our 'division of

(51)

the cake.' Instead of a knife they have a rake with which they draw the coins beyond the boundary or back to the heap, a procedure corresponding to the 'cutting off' and 'diminishing' of the slices. As the actions have to be accomplished by one movement of the rake, the result depends on the discernment and skill of the players.

There is a problem of division of seats in proportional polling. We shall explain it for three parties, A, B, and C, assuming that the proportion of votes registered is exactly reckoned and the seats in the Assembly proportionately distributed. To avoid fractions each party is first allowed as many seats as are indicated by the integral numbers; then the fractions are arranged according to their magnitude and each party receives a supplementary seat for its fraction in turn till all seats are distributed. For example, a district returns 5 members and counts 150,000 voters. The parties A, B, C

gathered 43,500, 69,000, and 37,500 votes respectively. Hence their claims are 1.45, 2.3, and 1.25 seats respectively. First they are given 1, 2, and 1 seats respectively and the remainders 0.45, 0.3, and 0.25 indicate that the fifth seat must fall to party A. The result of the election is therefore: $A-2$ seats, $B-2$ seats, $C-1$ seat. If we have an equilateral triangle (52) with a height of 5 inches, the sum of the distances of any given point in its interior from the three sides A, B, C will always be 5 inches. As there are 150,000 voters and 5 seats, we can represent a seat or 30,000 votes by one inch. By this convention every polling will be represented by a point in the triangle, the distances of the sides, A, B, C measured in inches giving

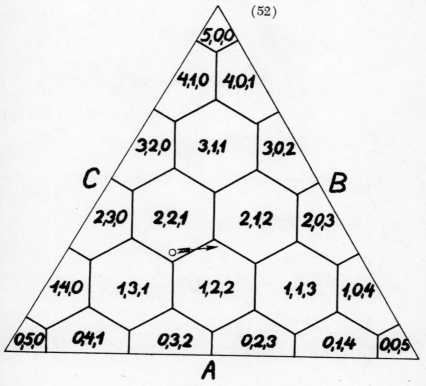

(52)

the number of seats won theoretically by the parties *A, B, C.* For instance, the point indicated by the spot corresponds to the result of the election as mentioned above, for its distances from the sides *A, B, C* are 1.45, 2.3, and 1.25 inches respectively. All those points that lead in practice to the same distribution of seats fill a regular hexagon; in our example this hexagon is indicated by 2, 2, 1. The distribution of seats being written in each hexagon, we may, by reckoning up the number of votes, obtain the final result of the election directly from the sketch, without computing the remainders. The arrow on the sketch shows how it can happen that, with the total of votes unchanged, party *A* can in the next election gain votes and lose a seat; this seat can be gained only by another party that has increased its votes. (Why?)

The system of distribution of seats adopted here is called the 'system of least remainders.' There are several other systems of proportional representation but

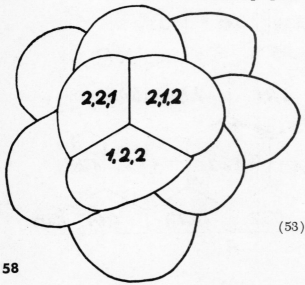

(53)

none of them escapes the paradox of a party's gaining votes and losing a seat. In fact, every system can be defined graphically (53) by a division of the triangle into regions, and if the system is to be fair, the map so obtained must present the same symmetrical view from all three vertices of the triangle. Thus the three regions (2, 2, 1), (1, 2, 2), and (2, 1, 2) must meet in the center of the triangle and their frontiers must be straight lines directed toward the vertices: this configuration already yields the paradox mentioned above.

Tessellations, Mixing of Liquids,

Measuring Areas and Lengths

OUR sketch of proportional elections reminds us of a honeycomb. The photograph (54) shows the plane filled up by hexagonal cells. No more than three hexagons meet in a point; this is the only case in which every

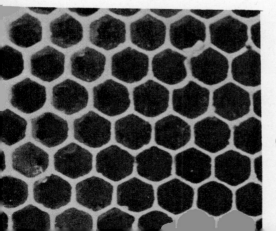

(54)

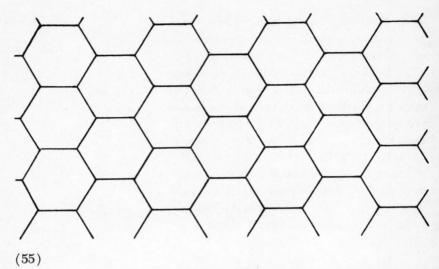

(55)

vertex is 'of degree three' (55); every other division exhibits points where more than three regions meet.

The tessellation with squares has been shown already as Fig. 10. By distortion we can get from it a tessellation with arbitrary quadrilaterals (56). The tessellation with triangles (57) is the last of this class; if we are restricted to only one shape and size of

(56)

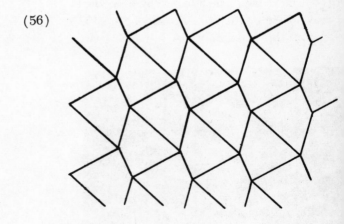

tile, this tile being a regular polygon, no other tessellation is possible. By using simultaneously various regular polygons to fill up the plane, each vertex being a common point of the same number of polygons of the same shape as those meeting in any other vertex, we obtain a homogeneous tessellation. As the angle of a regular n-gon equals $2-4/n$ right angles or $1/2-1/n$ of a complete angle, to determine the tessellation we must find positive integers n, p, q, r ... such as will give

$$1/2-1/n+1/2-1/p+1/2-1/q+\ldots=1.$$

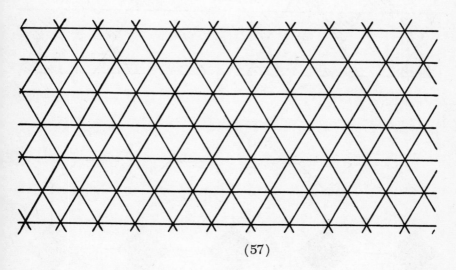

(57)

This way leads to 17 different patterns, but only 11 of these can be extended over the whole plane without overlapping. These are the three tessellations already mentioned and the eight following: (58), (59), (60), (61), (62), (63), (64), (65). Non-homogeneous tessellations are perhaps even more beautiful: (66), (67), (68A), (68B); their number is unlimited. (Why?)

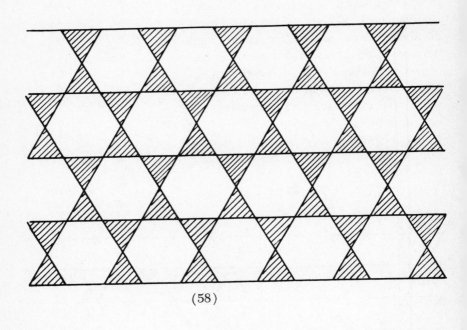

(58)

(59)

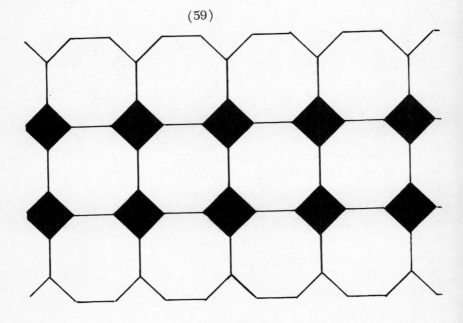

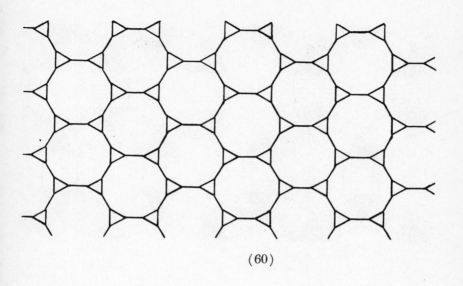

(60)

(61)

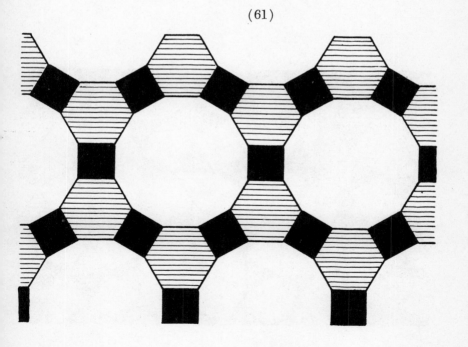

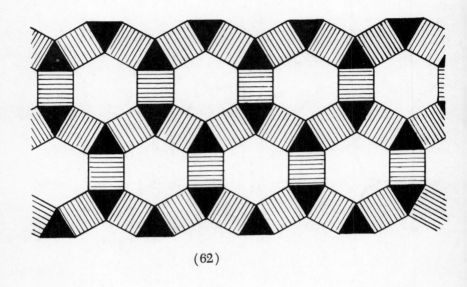

(62)

(63)

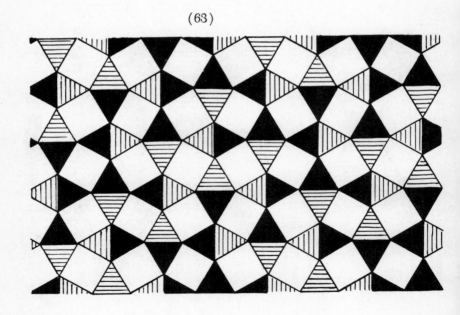

(64)

(65)

(66)

(67)

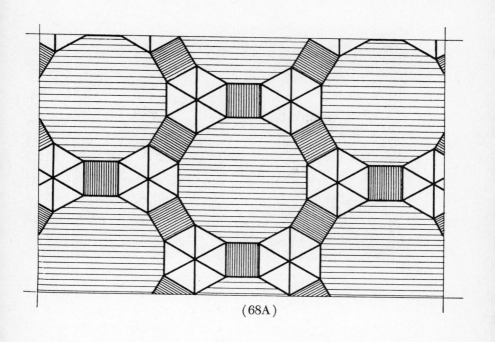

(68A)

(68B)

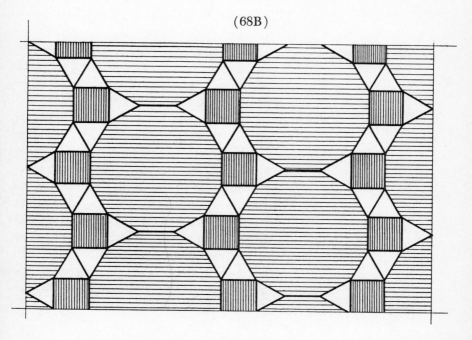

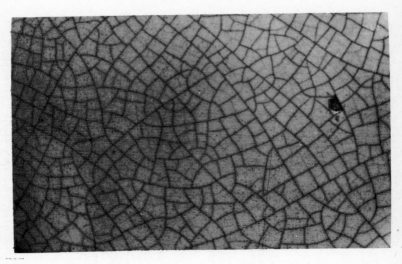

(69)

The patterns we observe on the shore of a river when the mud has been dried up by the sun or on tiles of earthenware (69) seem to be quite irregular; nevertheless as a rule they show right angles. This can be explained by assuming the breaking up of a layer of mud to be an effect of contraction; the line appearing as a fissure has, by a principle of mechanics, to make the work of disjunction as small as possible. The work is proportional to the areas of the sections and the lines must have a course such as to minimize the surfaces laid open by the fissure. This procedure gives right angles if the clay is homogeneous; the varying thickness of the layer accounts for the curvature of the lines. This remark supplies in many cases a means to decide which line appeared earlier and which later: the older of the two splits passes right through the point of junction. Thus we can follow the geneology of splits and eventually find the ancestors of the whole system.

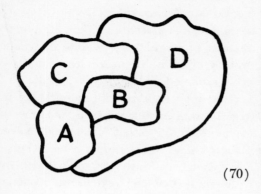

(70)

Suppose the pattern was composed initially of two regions, A and B. A new line appears, joining two points of two already existing arcs and giving rise to a new region C (70); since the new line breaks up two arcs into two parts each, the number of arcs increases by three. After n steps we have n more regions and $3n$ more lines. Since there were initially two regions and three lines, we now have $n+2$ regions and $3n+3$ lines. If we consider the exterior (the Ocean) as a region too, we have $n+3$ regions and $3n+3$ frontiers. Every frontier is common to two regions and, by drawing it, we increase the number of 'neighborships' by two: X-Y and Y-X. Thus we eventually have $6n+6$ 'neighborships,' and the average number of neighbors to a country is $(6n+6) / (n+3) = 6 - 12/(n+3)$. For an isle divided into k states the average number of neighbors to a state is $6 - 12/(k+1)$. (This number is less than 6 but tends to 6 as k increases. Disregarding the Ocean, we lose one region and at least 6 'neighborships,' since the number of states adjacent to the

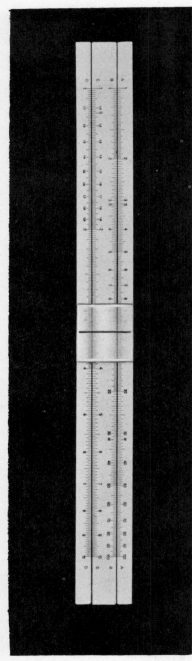

(71)

Ocean is at least 3, if we exclude the configuration of two states having two arcs as their common frontier. Thus the average number of neighbors to a state diminishes by this procedure and is still less than 6. We have excluded from our reasoning patterns with annular regions, with more than three regions meeting in a point, and with regions having several frontiers in common. Nevertheless, the average number of neighbors is less than 6 even for the general pattern, provided only that the regions are coherent domains; every new line creates one new region and the number of new arcs may now be 1, 2, or 3. They give at most 6 new 'neighborships'; if a cut through an annular region does not create a new region, it creates no new 'neighborship.' Thus our reasoning holds because the average number is, as for the restricted patterns, less than 6. The difference, however, is that our previous elimination of the Ocean does not work. Nevertheless, the average number is still less than 6 even if we count only firm land as regions and neighbors. This may be verified by inspecting different patterns, but the proof seems to be rather deep; the author cannot guarantee the exactness of the rule.

We must return to the Brahmin's chessboard. If we write on the left edge of every square of the upper row the number of grains contained in the square, we form a logarithmic scale. Such scales are to be found on the so-called 'logarithmic slide rule,' two above and two below; of these four scales the two central ones are engraved upon a movable rule (71). No matter what the position of the rule may be (72), the numbers standing immediately above each other are proportional. Here, for instance, the numbers on the fixed upper scale are 2.45 times greater than those on the margin immediately beneath them, so that if, for example, we wish to multiply 3.45 by 2.45, we move the window with the hair to 3.45 on the margin and read off above 8.45 as the product. On the lower scales we see 1.565, 1.86, 2.91. The error amounts to about 0.3 per cent. The numbers on the uppermost scale are squares of the numbers standing beneath them on the lowest scale. The hair indicator on the photograph shows $2.91^2 = 8.45$. It is therefore possible to extract the square root by means of the slide rule. (How?) The slide rule is especially useful to solve rule-of-three problems.

When mixing two liquids of different specific gravities, e.g. two kinds of gasoline, we can use the following nomogram (73) to determine the specific gravity of the mixture. The broad, oblique scale on the sketch is movable; at the point where it intersects the left-hand vertical line we read the specific gravity of the lighter liquid; at the point where it cuts the right-hand vertical line, we get the specific weight of the heavier liquid, while the fixed oblique scale shows in the intersection with the movable one the specific gravity of the mixture on the movable scale and the percentage of the heavier liquid on itself. To compute the specific gravity of a mixture composed of 55 per cent oil with specific gravity .830,

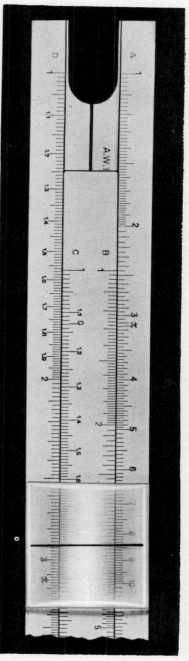

(72)

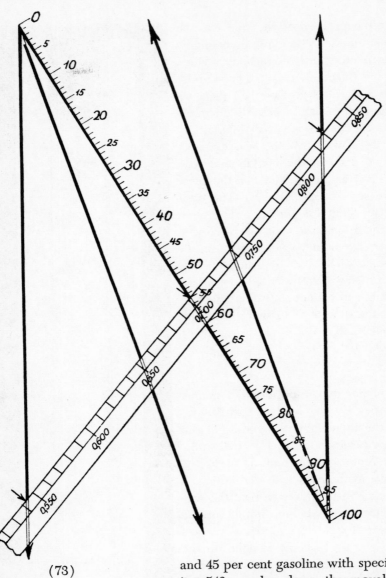

(73)

and 45 per cent gasoline with specific gravity .543, we lay down the movable scale with the points .830 and .543 on the vertical lines and shift it vertically until it crosses the point 55 on the fixed scale; in this very point we read from the movable scale .701, which is the specific gravity of the mixture we had to find out. The theory results from the similarity of triangles formed by the scales. The two oblique, heavy lines must be used if the specific gravities of the components have a difference less than 20 per cent; their role is the same as that of the verticals. Knowing any three of the data we can find the fourth; for instance, the specific gravities of both components and that of the mixture being given, the nomogram yields easily the percentage of the components. (How?)

(74)

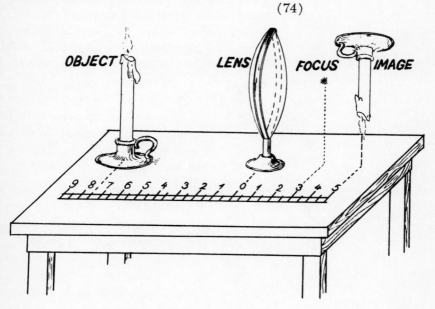

There are simpler nomograms known. Such is the nomogram of the lens. The distance f, g, h of the object, the picture, and the focus from the lens (74) are connected according to an optical law by the formula $1/f + 1/g = 1/h$ and, by drawing a straight line through two of these numbers

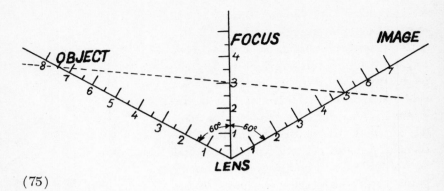

on the nomogram (75), we can find the third. Here, for instance, the object is at the distance of 7.5 inches, the focus is 3 inches from the lens, hence the image will be 5 inches behind the lens. We can apply this nomogram to the question of the time *h* necessary to accomplish a task by joint effort of two men, who would need separately *f* and *g* hours for it. (If a man needs 5 hours to fill a car with coal and his apprentice 7.5 hours for the same job, they will do it together in 3 hours.)

It is possible to draw nomograms without providing them with scales of numbers. If we notice that the musical scale is a logarithmic one, i.e. similar to the scales on the slide rule (Fig. 71), for the number of vibrations keeps rising by a constant factor as we pass one tone higher, we can construct the following nomogram (76), which permits us to read the radius of one meter of wire weighted by 100 kilograms, provided the material and the pitch are given. For example, the dotted line on the column indicates the radius of an iron wire tuned to 'A.' Inversely, material and radius being

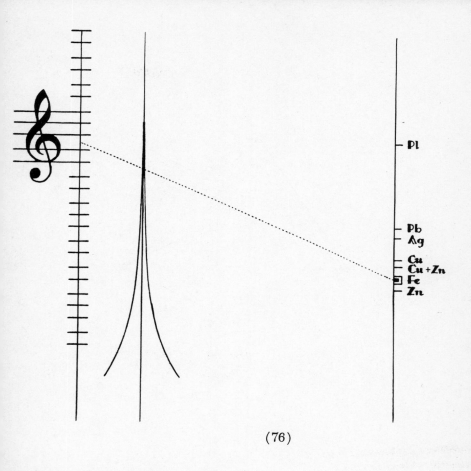

(76)

given, we may also ascertain the pitch of the note. The construction is based on Mersenne's formula

$$n = \frac{1}{2Lr}\sqrt{\frac{P}{d\pi}}$$

(n number of vibrations per second, L length in meters, P stretching force in kilograms, r radius of the section in millimeters, d density of the material in grams per cm^3, $\pi = 3.14159\ldots$). The spaces between the music lines are greater where there occurs a major third (as, for instance, $G\text{-}B$).

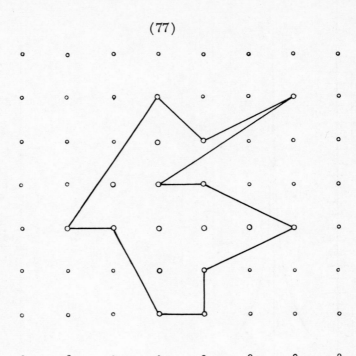

The polygon on the lattice of whole numbers (77) illustrates the following theorem: the area of any polygon whose vertices are points of the lattice is equal to the number of interior lattice points, plus half the number of lattice points on the border, minus 1. For instance, in the present case the area is

$$6 + \frac{11}{2} - 1 = 10.5.$$

We can verify it easily for a rectangle. If its base is m units and its height n units, its area is mn units. On the border there are 4 vertices, $2(m-1)$ points on both bases, and $2(n-1)$ points on both vertical sides: together there are $b=2m+2n$ border points. The interior points form $m-1$ columns and $n-1$ rows; there are $i=(m-1)(n-1)$ interior points. The rule gives for the area A the numer $i+b/2-1$ equal to

$$(m-1)\ (n-1)+\tfrac{1}{2}(2m+2n)-1=mn,$$

which is the true value. The next step is the observation that two polygons with a common side can be combined into one polygon by suppressing that side, and that the number $i+b/2-1$ for the new polygon equals the sum of the analogous numbers corresponding to the component polygons. It follows that the number $i+b/2-1$ corresponding to a triangle resulting from halving a rectangle by its diagonal is one half of the number corresponding to the rectangle and therefore equal to the area of the triangle. Now we can get every polygon by adding and subtracting appropriate triangles and finally we get the rule

$$A=i+b/2-1$$

for every polygon with vertices on the lattice.

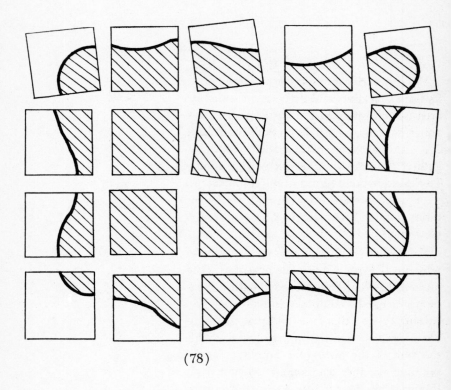

(78)

To measure areas we can utilize the lattice of whole numbers even for arbitrary domains. We can always shift a domain to such a position that the number of lattice points covered by the domain equals or surpasses the area of the domain. For example (78) the shaded area has 11 units. Let us place it as we please on the lattice and cut along the lines of the lattice. The whole figure breaks up into squares; placing them one upon another (79), we shall be able to pierce the pile with a pin so as to strike the shaded parts at least 11 times. To explain it, let us supose that we can strike

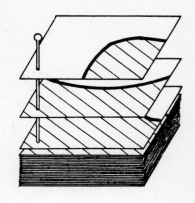

the shaded parts 10 times at most; then the basic square would be covered at most 10 times by the shaded parts and the whole domain would have an area at most equal to 10 units, contrary to our knowledge. Having discovered a point with the required property, we spread the squares beside one another again (80) and we see 11 (or more) pin pricks in the domain; then we move the domain, shifting it in such a way that one pin prick covers a lattice-point; then all of them will. Our argument is valid also for a domain with an area of 10.1 units. (Why?)

(80)

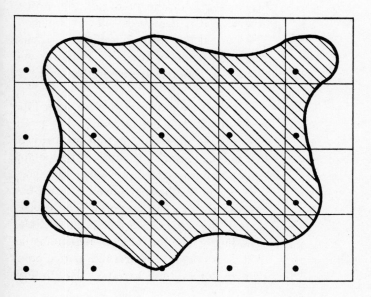

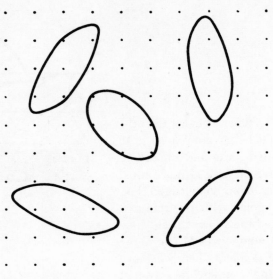

(81)

Let us take a convex curved line of an area 4, having a center, i.e. a point that halves all chords through it. Now let us place this curved line on the lattice of integers (81) in such a way that the center becomes one of the points of the lattice; otherwise it is immaterial how it is placed. The curved line will now enclose at least two more points of the lattice. This is one of Minkowski's discoveries in geometry.

We shall make use of this theorem (the proof of which is not obvious) to estimate how far we may see through an array of hop-poles. We are supposed to be looking from a point occupied previously by a hop-pole, which we have removed to place our eye exactly in a lattice point. The projections of the hop-poles are (82) little circles of radius r. The line of sight reaches as far as it does not come nearer to a lattice point than r. Let us draw a straight line through

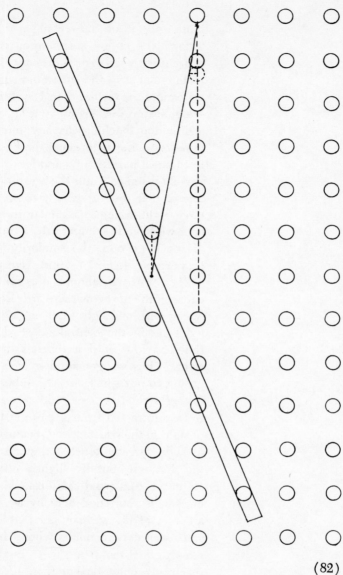

(82)

our observation point, extending to the distance $1/r$ on both sides, and let us consider
this segment as the median of a rectangle
with $2r$ as base. The area of the rectangle is
4 and its center is a lattice point; by Minkowski's theorem at least two lattice points

more will fall on the rectangle or in its interior. The circles surrounding them will consequently touch or cut the median of the rectangular strip and cut off our sight. Thus we cannot see farther than $1/r$. But we can see almost as far. To prove it let us look in a direction touching the next circle in the same row. Let us prolong the line of sight to the next parallel row and let us compute at what distance it cuts the central (dashed) line of that row. It is easy to see that the large right triangle is similar to the small one; we have to compute the hypotenuse h of the large one: the similarity gives the proportion $h:1=1:r$ and consequently $h=1/r$. But we cannot see as far as h, because in the next row there are circles interfering with our sight. Let us move such a circle along the central (dashed) line of the next row until it touches the line of sight. Thus we get another triangle, congruent to our small one. Its side along the line of sight is $\sqrt{1-r^2}$ and this amount is to be subtracted from $1/r$ to get the range of sight in the worst case. Of course our line of sight already touches a small circle in the first row, but by slightly altering the angle we can avoid this obstacle, and our outlook is shortened only by a very small amount. Thus we can say that our sight can reach certain points whose distance is almost equal to $1/r-\sqrt{1-r^2}$, but it cannot reach any point farther than $1/r$. For instance, when the poles have a diameter of 2 inches and are standing 20 inches apart, we have, taking 20 inches as our unit, $r=0.05$; we get $1/r=20$ units$=400$ inches and $1/r-\sqrt{1-r^2}=19.0013$ units$=380.026$ inches. Thus the farthest point visible has a distance between 380.026 and 400 inches.

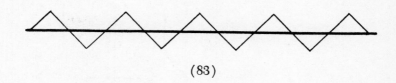

(83)

The measuring of areas is easier than the measuring of lengths. This is so because if a contour is given with a certain accuracy, we can estimate the area enclosed by it with an error that becomes less and less as the accuracy increases and can be made as small as we like. It is quite a different matter with lengths. Two curved lines lying very near one another can differ considerably in their lengths: the zigzag line (83), for instance, is about 40 per cent longer than the straight one. There are lines of infinite length, if we admit the existence of things defined correctly in mathematical language and do not care for real models. Mathematicians need such curves for theoretical purposes. Such a theoretical problem, for instance, is how to draw a curve passing through every point of a square, when we mean by 'square' all points of the interior and the boundary. Sierpiński solves the problem by beginning with a closed polygon (84), then uniting four similar polygons (85) into one cross, after which he joins four figures similar to the cross (86), and so on (87), repeating (88) the construction. The limit of these approximations is the curved line filling the square:

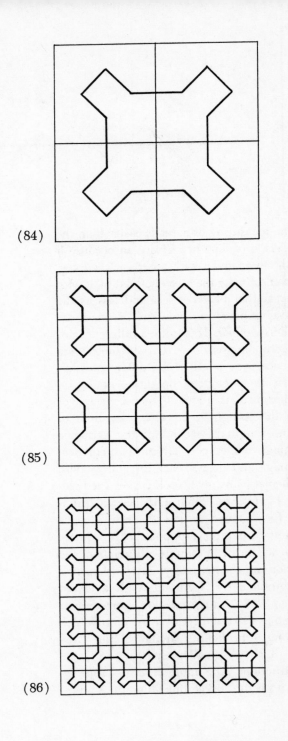

(84)

(85)

(86)

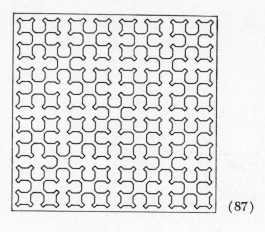

(87)

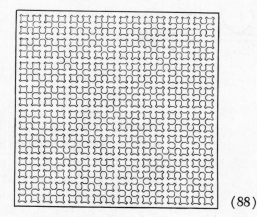

(88)

we may regard it as the track of a moving point, and for every point in the square indicate the precise moment when the moving point will pass through that given point. The curve has an infinite length. It is impossible, however, to draw it in its final perfect stage. (Why?)

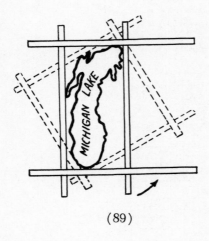

(89)

Given any closed curve, like Lake Michigan, for instance, we can circumscribe a square about it. This fact is easy to see, because we can (89) first circumscribe a rectangle by taking a pair of parallel tangents, and another parallel pair orthogonal to the first one, and the turn of the whole frame round the fixed curve; after a rotation of 90° the pairs are interchanged and if the distance of the first pair was originally greater than that of the second, it became finally less. There must therefore be a moment when both distances are equal and just at that moment the tangents form a square.

It is much more difficult to prove that we can inscribe a square in any closed contour; nevertheless (90) it is true.

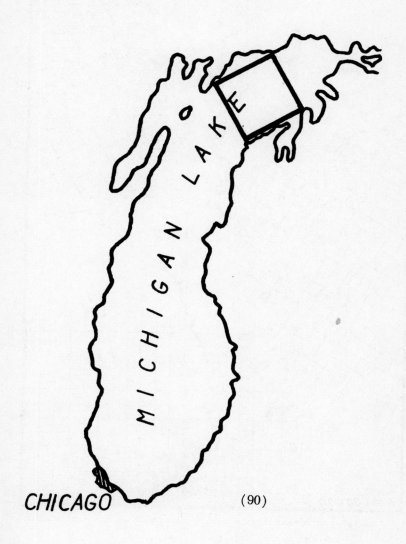

CHICAGO   (90)

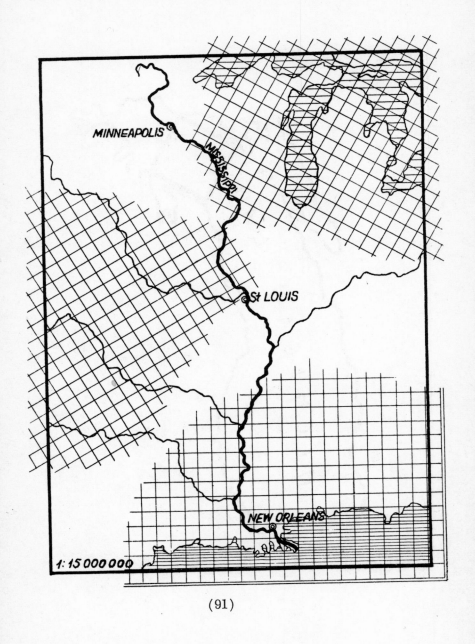

(91)

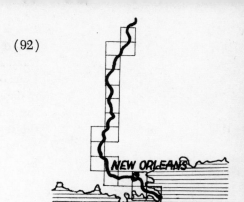

To measure lengths we can make use of
a sort of chessboard. On a transparent sheet
there is a lattice of straight lines forming
squares with sides 3.82 mm. One family of
lines is inclined 30° to the frame of the
sheet. To measure the length of the Mississippi River, for instance, we put the frame
of the sheet on the frame of the map (91)
and travel along the river, from its source
to the sea, as if the end of our pencil were
a rook (92) wandering on a chessboard.
Counting the steps, we then put the sheet
with one of its lines on the frame of the map
and do as before, finally proceeding as we
did the first time but with the sheet reversed. The total number of steps gives the
length in mm; as the map is 1: 15,000,000,
we have to multiply the total by 15 to get
the length of the Mississippi in kilometers
(or by 9.321 to get it in miles).

To explain how this *longimeter* works, let
us measure a straight segment of L millimeters. The number of rook's steps along
the segment is simply the sum of projections of the segment on both directions of
the lattice, when we take the side of the

89

squares as a unit. Putting the longimeter in three positions, we get the sum of projections on six different directions; it is easy to realize from our sketch that these directions form a star with 30° between its rays. If the segment initially made an angle α with a line of the longimeter, the six angles will be

$$\alpha+0°, \ \alpha+30°, \ \alpha+60°, \ \alpha+90°,$$
$$\alpha+120°, \ \alpha+150°.$$

The sum of the projections will be

$$L\{\sin(\alpha+0°)+\sin(\alpha+30°)+\sin(\alpha+60°)$$
$$+\sin(\alpha+90°)+\sin(\alpha+120°)+\sin(\alpha$$
$$+150°)\}.$$

We don't know α but we find that the expression above becomes least for $\alpha=0°$ and greatest for $\alpha=15°$. Thus the least value is

$$L(0+1/2+\sqrt{3}/2+1+\sqrt{3}/2+1/2)=3.732L,$$

and the greatest value is

$$L\left(\frac{\sqrt{6}-\sqrt{2}}{4}+\frac{\sqrt{2}}{2}+\frac{\sqrt{6}+\sqrt{2}}{4}+\frac{\sqrt{6}+\sqrt{2}}{4}+\right.$$
$$\left.\frac{\sqrt{2}}{2}+\frac{\sqrt{6}-\sqrt{2}}{4}\right)=3.852L.$$

As our unit is 3.82, we have to divide the results by 3.82 to get the sums of projections in mm. We get now $0.977L$ and $1.011L$ instead of L. Thus we get the length of every segment with an error between −2.3 and 1.1 per cent. As we can consider every curve as composed of short straight segments, the relative error of its length as computed by the longimeter will not exceed these limits; in most cases it will be even smaller. (Why?)

On some maps contour lines are drawn to show the vertical configuration of the land. By measuring their total length, one can compute the average declivity of the district. This can be done with the aid of the longimeter by counting the number of intersections of the lattice with the lines.

There still remains the question of the length of a line given by nature and not by a mathematical definition. When measuring the length of a river, one is faced with the problem of small sinuosities of its course. Some countries have as their frontiers such tortuous rivers or mountain ridges. By employing more and more detailed maps and increasing the accuracy of measurement to a corresponding degree, we can get the length to be about as great as we like. The longimeter is a remedy for this inconvenience, but the drawback of the device is that its accuracy is limited by the size of the real square corresponding (for a given map) to the longimeter's square. This size may vary, and it would be difficult to give definite rules; such rules would prescribe different scales and appropriate longimeters for different purposes. There is, however, the method of measuring lengths by counting the number n of intersections of a set of parallel lines with the curve considered; if d is the distance of the lines and k the number of different positions of the set, then $L = nd\pi/2k$ is the approximate length. We have to turn the transparent sheet carrying the lines through an angle of $180°/k$ from one position to the next. To avoid the paradox of length noted above, we can agree to discard on every line its 11th and subsequent intersections with the curve. Thus we get what may be called L_{10}, the length of order 10. This concept is free from the paradox of length; if we employ more and more detailed maps and increase the accuracy of measurement by reducing d and increasing k, keeping the restriction to 10 intersections at most per line, the numbers L computed by the formula above will approach more and more closely a definite limit, the ideal value of L_{10}. In the same manner lengths of any order L_1, $L_2, \ldots, L_m, \ldots$ could be defined. This principle opens a way to rules of measuring that are free from such units as miles or yards: to compare the lengths of frontiers, the length of order 12, for instance, could be adopted for all countries.

Let us call L'_m the length of the left bank of the Mississippi, L''_m the length of the right bank, both of the mth order; we still have the paradox

$$\lim_{m \to \infty} L'_m = \infty, \ \lim_{m \to \infty} L''_m = \infty.$$

Nevertheless, we can reasonably expect the limit of the ratio L'_m/L''_m to be finite. This limit can be measured to any desired accuracy: we have only to choose m sufficiently great and apply the method described above. Thus we could measure the ratio of the lengths of both banks without determining the true lengths themselves. We leave it to the reader to explain the meaning of L_2 for the boundary of a region.

Shortest Paths, Locating Schools, and Pursuing Ships

THE straight line is the shortest path. An Arab wishes to return to his tent, but on the way he wants to feed his horse and draw water from a river. Which is he to do first? (93) The tent reflected in the river's bank gives a point a_1, while this point reflected in turn in the border of the pasture gives a_2. When the order of successive reflections is reversed, we obtain A_1 and A_2. The black, full, zigzag line is the shortest way; it is equal to the distance of point a_2 from the Arab's position. If he wished to water his horse first, the path would be at least as long as the distance in a straight line to A_2, which is more. The Arab did not draw any plan; he simply aimed his musket at the point where the pasture and the river meet, and seeing that point lying on the left of his tent, rode off to the left. To explain his behavior let us remark first that the points a_2 and A_2 can be found without knowing the position of the Arab. All his possible positions can be classified as those nearer to a_2, those nearer to A_2, and those equally distant from a_2 and A_2. The last positions form a straight line and, as for an Arab standing at the intersection point of river and pasture both solutions give the same length of travel, the straight line passes through that point. For an Arab already in the tent both solutions give the same length;

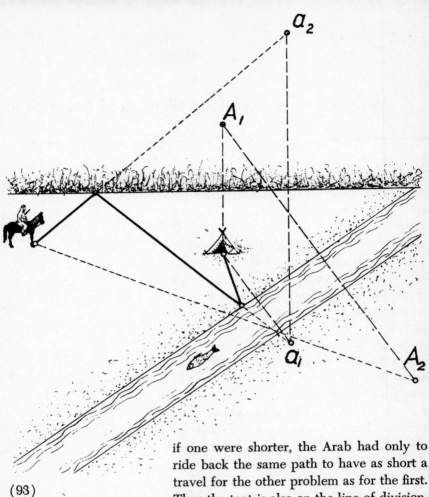

(93)

if one were shorter, the Arab had only to ride back the same path to have as short a travel for the other problem as for the first. Thus the tent is also on the line of division. It passes, therefore, through the intersection of pasture and river and through the tent. The Arab, seeing the intersection to the left of the tent, is himself to the left of the division line, and, consequently, nearer to a_2 than to A_2. As the shortest paths are as long as his distances from a_2 and A_2, he chooses the itinerary drawn on our picture and equal to his distance from a_2. The principle of reflection employed here is the same as in our billiard problems.

Three villages are to build a common school. In order to reduce as far as possible the total time spent by pupils in going to school, they have to find an appropriate spot for the location of the school. They have, for instance, 50, 70, and 90 children respectively. Stretching out the map of the district on a table (94), we make holes in the table where the villages are, pass three strings through the holes, tie the upper ends into a knot, and weight the lower ones with 50, 70, and 90 ounces respectively. The school should be built where the knot is caught. But the spoiling of the table is not necessary. We first draw a triangle (95) with sides 50, 70, and 90 units (choosing any unit we like): we are interested in the external angles ⪤, ⪤, and ⪥ of this auxiliary triangle. Now we have to find on the

(94)

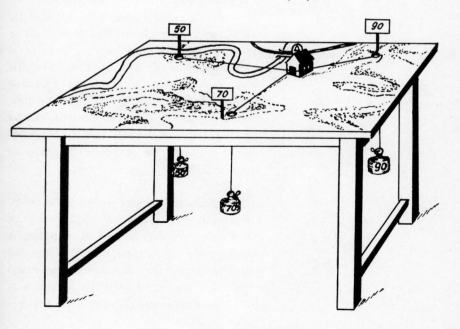

95

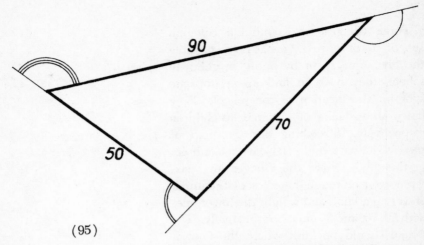

(95)

map a point from which the villages are visible in directions that form the same angles. So, for instance, the villages 50 and 90 have to be seen (96) at the same angle as the external angle enclosed by the sides 50 and 90 of the auxiliary triangle. The points on the map responding to this condition lie on a circle through the villages 50 and 90, and the center of the circle is easily found from the proposition that the central angle corresponding to both villages equals twice the internal angle of the auxiliary triangle. Having drawn the circle, we proceed in the same way with villages 50 and 70; we get a second circle and the intersection of both circles gives the location of the school.

As to the first device of weights and holes, it results from the laws of statics that the equilibrium of the system of weights is possible only when their center of gravity is as low as possible. This center moves up or down when we change the length of a string by displacing the knot; its vertical

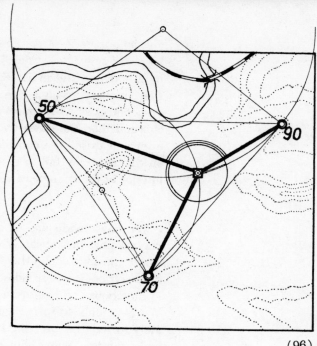

(96)

travel is proportional to the increase of the piece of string beneath the table multiplied by the weight it carries. Thus, the center of mass is as low as possible when the sum of the products of the pieces of strings above the table by the attached weights is as small as possible. But this happens exactly when the sum of the ways to school is smallest, because this sum equals the sum of the products of length of string and weight (we can assume one inch on the map for a mile in reality and one ounce for a child — then the sum of lengths of string multiplied by weights equals the sum of ways in miles).

The procedure with holes and strings has the advantage of always giving a good solution, even if one of the weights is so great that the other two together are not able to oppose its stress. In such a case the knot — if sufficiently thick — will be caught by a hole and still indicate the right place. The auxiliary triangle can fail because it does not exist when one village has more children than the other two together. But even if it exists, the construction of circles on the map may fail to give a point in the interior of the triangle of villages. (Why?)

We have made use of a principle that plays a part in statics: When three forces counterbalance each other, it is possible to draw a triangle whose sides will correspond, in directions and lengths, with those forces. We have only to turn Figure 95 appropriately to see that we have applied the principle quoted, going, however, backward, from the triangle to the forces. This remark leads to the so-called reciprocal figures of Cremona. If we have, for example (97), 10 rods bound together by pins at points A, B, C, D, E, O, we obtain 6 areas: 1, 2, 3, 4, 5, 6. Now let us draw the reciprocal figure (98) or the scheme of forces. The areas will now be indicated by letters, the vertices by numbers. In Figure 97 the vertex C is common to areas 2, 3, and 6 and unites the rods BC, OC, DC; in Figure 98 the area C has 2, 3, 6 as vertices and adjoins the areas B, O, D, the boundaries BC, OC, DC being parallel to the rods BC, OC, DC of Figure 97. In this manner the whole scheme is constructed. Supposing that, at joint C of the rods, forces act in the direction of the arrows, their magnitudes being equal to the corresponding sides of the triangle C of the scheme, they will be

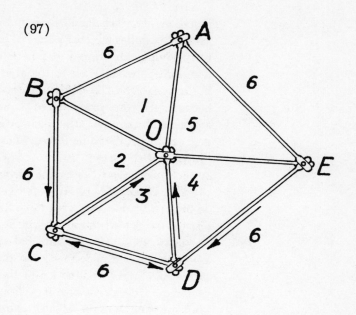

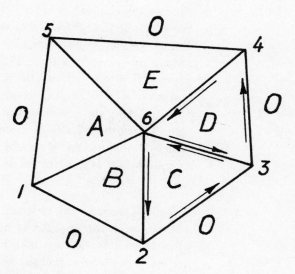

found to counterbalance each other. The principle applies to other points of junction. For example, the forces at junction D are determined by the sides of the area D, but the arrow in rod CD now points toward D, because, by the principle of equality of action and reaction, the rod pushing C pushes D with the same force. Thus having drawn first the arrows in the area C of the scheme, we have to draw the arrow 6-3 in the area D contrary to arrow 3-6 in area C; as the arrows in every area have to form a circuit, we get all the arrows in D, then in E, and so on. Thus we can make out the whole scheme, provided we know the length of one side and the direction of the corresponding arrow. Hence it follows that, knowing one tension of the construction Figure 97, we can find all the others. When this tension changes, it is only the size, not the shape of the scheme, that will change. Hence we see, for instance, that rod OE is always submitted to a force 26/15 times as great as that to which rod BC is submitted, and is pulled if BC is compressed. (Why?) When seeking the place for the school, we started with the scheme of forces and then found the shape of the system of linked rods in equilibrium (the strings were our rods).

The problem of the shortest path arises when there is the question of pursuit. It is obvious that the best method of pursuit on an indefinite plane (ocean) is to take a course straight toward the object pursued. Nevertheless, the meaning of 'best method' is not immediately clear. If we know, for

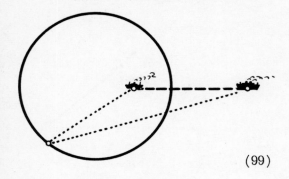

(99)

instance, that the vessel pursued does not know that it is the object of our pursuit, and that, consequently, it will keep its course whatever we do, we can do better than to steer right toward him. If we know the ratio $V:v$ of both velocities, we can find the straight course that assures the capture of our prey in the shortest time possible. We have only to find all points that can be reached simultaneously by both ships from their actual positions; they form a circle (99) (the so-called circle of Apollonius). If this circle cuts the course of the pursued vessel, we have to steer directly toward the point of intersection; if it does not cut the course, it is impossible to catch the fugitive.

In this last case we may try to approach the enemy as close as possible; supposing his velocity v greater than our V and his course at a right angle to the direction in which we first observed him (100), the simple construction of our sketch shows the best line of approach; at the moment of least distance the pursued ship appears right ahead. (Why?)

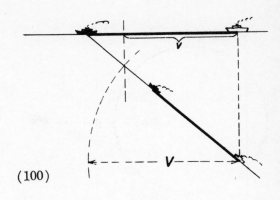

(100)

But it could happen that the captain of the other vessel takes notice of our design and changes his course; then the methods based on his ignorance lose their advantage. To define the 'best method' we must therefore reckon not with the best conditions but with the worst, as in chess and other games. Let us call the pursuer White, the pursued Black, the velocity of White V, the velocity of Black v and let V be greater than v. The efficiency of a method of pursuit can be measured by the time interval from the start to the capture; the shorter this interval, the better the method. On an infinite ocean, Black can keep to the simple 'rule of thumb': whatever method White chooses, to steer straight away from him. Then the relative speed of White, that is, the speed with which he approaches Black, will be $V-v$ or less, and the time necessary to capture will be $d/(V-v)$ or more, if d denotes the initial distance. Thus White cannot guarantee a shorter time than $d/(V-v)$, because Black, by using the rule of thumb, can enjoy his freedom at least during this time; he will remain free for a longer time if White does not always steer directly toward him. On the other side, White can guarantee to catch Black after the time $d/(V-v)$ at most; he has only to keep his prow always directed toward Black and to go full-speed ahead. He will make even better time if Black does not stick to his rule of thumb or if he reduces speed. Now we have the right to call the rule 'right ahead on Black' the best method for White and the rule 'right ahead from White' the best method for Black. When using his best method, White can guarantee the time $d/(V-v)$ but by no other method can he guarantee a better time. Black can, by using his best method, guarantee the time of freedom $d/(V-v)$, but by no other method can he guarantee a better, i.e. a longer, time. As the result $d/(V-v)$ is the same for both partners, the game of pursuit is a *closed* game. To realize how the pursuit can be considered as a *just* game, we have only to stipulate that d, the distance, being measured in miles, V and v in knots, White has to pay to Black the amount $T-d/(V-v)$ dollars, T being the number of hours from start to capture; if the amount is negative, it is Black who pays.

The pursuit is more complicated if the encounter happens close to shore (101). If the shore is a straight line (or approximately a straight line), the best methods are as follows. The circle of Apollonius, as defined previously, is to be traced on the map; it moves with the ships. So long as it does not cut the shore, the same methods as on an

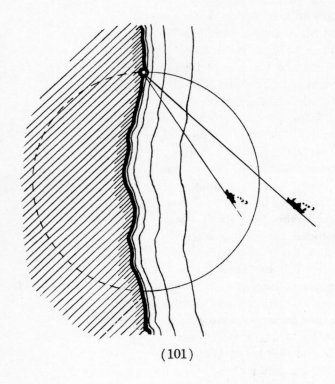

(101)

open sea are the best, but when it cuts the
shore, the best method for both ships is to
point always toward the farther of the two
intersections. If both keep to this rule, they
will keep a steady course, but if one (or
both) does not obey it, the point will wander along the shore; the ship that obeys the
rule will in this case have a variable course.
The neighborhood of the shore reduces the
best time, and it is therefore advantageous
for the pursuer. It is interesting that 'neighborhood' has here a definite meaning: the
coast is near if the circle of Apollonius cuts
it.

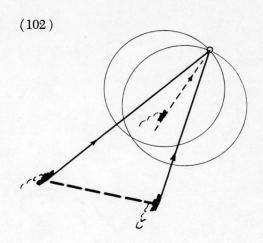

For two ships pursuing a third we have to trace two circles of Apollonius, one for each pursuer. The positions of both pursuers and the farther of the two points where the circles intersect each other are vertices of a triangle. If the escaping ship is in the interior (102) of the triangle, the best method for all three ships is to point toward the third vertex; if the fugitive is beyond (103) the triangle, the best method for the pursuers is the standard method of

(103)

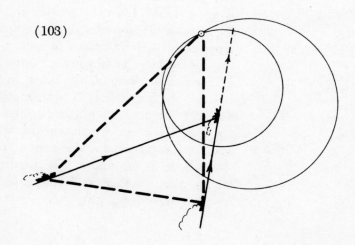

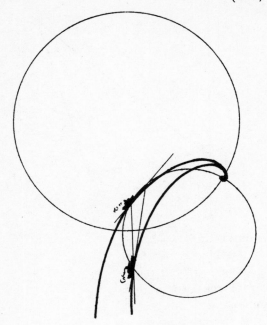

steering toward the prey; as to the fugitive, he has to compute the time of capture by the formula $d/(V-v)$ for both pursuers, to decide which danger is more imminent and to fly straight away from the more dangerous ship. It is to be remembered that the triangle changes and the fugitive may cross its sides. This cannot happen if the fugitive has been initially in the interior and all three ships keep to the rules; in this case all ships will have a steady course. (Why?) The problem of two pursuers has not been solved by a complete mathematical reasoning; it is for the reader to prove or to disprove the results above; it is an interesting question, whether the definition of 'surrounding the enemy' given here is correct.

Suppose one ship pursues another and keeps always a constant angle with the line connecting both ships, and suppose the fugitive does the same, steering at a certain constant angle from the connecting line. Then both will travel on curves winding themselves round a common (104) vortex. To find this vortex, which is obviously the point of capture, we trace the circle of Apollonius for the initial position of both ships, a circle passing through these positions, and the point where their directions meet. The circles cut each other in two points; the farther one is the vortex sought for. The radii joining the vortex to the ships make angles with their directions, which are the same for both ships; this follows from the vortex lying on the second circle. The distances from ships to vortex have the ratio $V:v$ because the vortex lies on the circle of Apollonius. It follows therefrom that the triangle ship-vortex drawn for the initial position and the one drawn after a short time with the initial vortex are similar; the bases of the triangles are at both times the lines joining the ships. As the ships keep both their angles against this base, it is obvious that the relative situations of the ships and of their directions to the vortex are similar at both times; as V and v are constant, the new vortex will consequently cover the initial one. Viewed from this point, the angular distance of the ships will remain constant, and the paths will cut the radii issuing from the vortex at a constant angle, the same for both. Now,

*This angular distance equals the angle formed by the directions of ships, as can be seen from the second circle.

(105)

we have a name for a curve cutting the radii at a constant angle: it is (105) a *logarithmic spiral*. If we turn the book about the vortex, the spiral seems to grow larger or smaller. Two spirals having the same constant angle with the radii are congruent. This is the case for the two paths of ships in Figure 104.

Let us suppose that the captain of the pursuing ship is doing his best, i.e. pointing straight at the enemy, who prefers the pirate's trick of always taking a course at right angles to the course of the pursuer.

Of course, as already explained, both will travel along congruent logarithmic spirals. If the initial distance was d and the velocity of the pursuer v, the time elapsing from the start to the moment of capture is d/v, whatever the velocity V of the fugitive may be, because the fugitive's speed does not contribute to the mutual distance. The length of the spiral from its vortex to the initial position of the pursuer is therefore d. This being true at any moment, the length of the pursuer's spiral from its actual position to the vortex always equals the distance from ship to ship. The ships always subtend a right angle at the vortex (because the angular distance equals the angle formed by the directions of the ships, as can be seen from the second circle). Is it possible (106) that both ships may trace the same path? The answer depends only on the ratio V/v. If it is 3.644, both ships will travel on the same path and — what seems very strange — the fugitive, whose speed is greater, wanders on the far-water of the pursuer and finally collides with him. The logarithmic

(106)

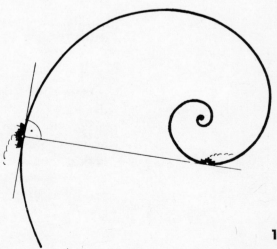

spiral thus obtained has the peculiar property of being its own evolute: it can be traced by a thread winding itself on the same spiral. We have only to consider the line joining the ships on our sketch as a thread of invariable length, the greater ship winding it round the spiral, as she travels along the next coil of the same spiral. The vortex is always $74°40'$ away from the prow.

Three dogs A, B, and C start at vertices of an equilateral triangle, running with the same speed v, A toward B, B toward C, and C toward A. A approaches B at a rate v, due to his own speed, but as B runs toward C, a component of B's velocity brings him nearer to A. This component equals $v/2$ because $\cos 60° = 1/2$. Thus $3v/2$ is the speed of mutual approach of A and B. If s is the initial distance AB, the duration of pursuit will be $s:3v/2=2s/3v$. The three dogs continue to form an equilateral triangle. As in the case of the ships, they travel along logarithmic spirals. The length of each spiral is time $\times$ velocity:

$$(2s/3v) \times v = 2s/3,$$

and the meeting point is the center of the initial triangle.

In unwinding thread from a round bobbin there arises another kind of spiral (107): the evolute of the circle. If we can imagine an object suddenly freeing itself from the laws of gravitation (and resistance of the air), we should see it flying away from us and describing exactly the same spiral.

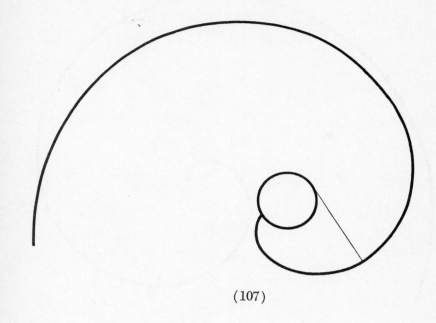

(107)

(Why?) Supposing a fly crawls along the radius of a uniformly revolving gramophone record with a uniform velocity, it will be describing another kind of spiral, the so-called spiral of Archimedes (108). Here the length of the radius-vector is proportional to the angle of that radius with a fixed direction. A heart composed of two arcs of such a spiral (109) and fixed upon the face of a disc will change the uniform, rotating motion of the disc into the uniform, to-and-fro motion of a piston. (Why?)

(108)

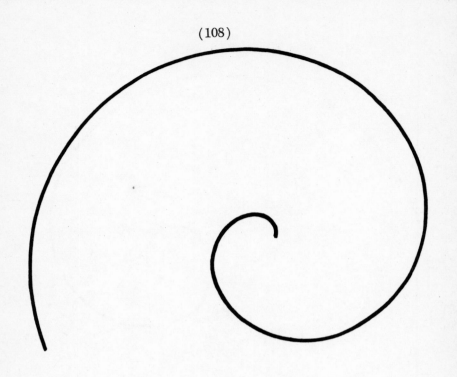

(109)

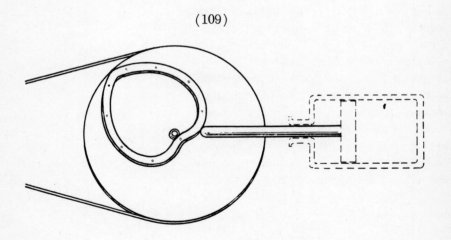

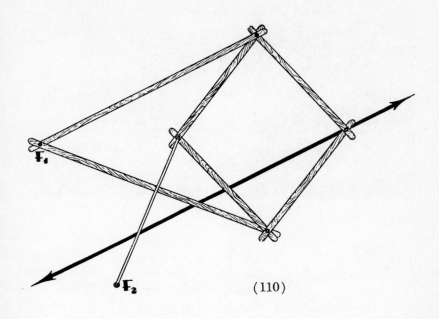

(110)

Straight Lines, Circles, Symmetry, and Optical Illusions

A polygon made of rods may assist us in drawing a straight line without the help of a ruler. The *inversor* (110) consists of six rods, of which the four shorter ones are equal and form a movable rhombus, while the two long ones — also equal — connect the vertices of the rhombus with the fixed point F_1. When the other fixed point F_2 is joined to the third vertex of the rhombus by the seventh rod — equal to F_1F_2 in length — and all junctions are movable, the free vertex, when we deform the rhombus, traces a straight segment.

(111)

To determine the centroid of a stick, we place it horizontally (111) on the edges of our palms and then we bring our hands closer together; finally (112) they meet in the center of gravity. The stick never loses its equilibrium because when the centroid, which is initially between the palms, approaches one of them, the pressure on the nearer palm becomes many times greater than the pressure on the other palm; its

(112)

product by the coefficient of friction must finally surpass the analogous product for the other palm; when this happens, the relative movement of the first palm ceases and the relative movement of the other one starts. This play continues alternately until both palms meet; the centroid is always between them and it is there at the final stage. The trick is done automatically without any conscious effort.

(113)

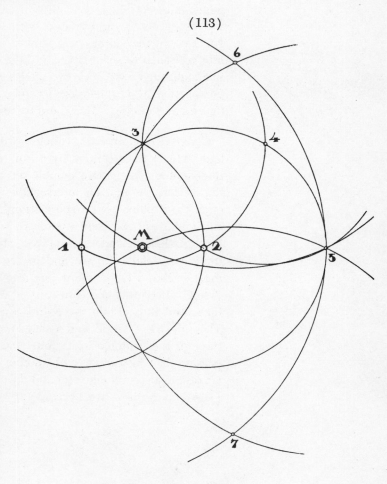

Any construction for the tracing of which the compass and ruler are used may be drawn without the help of the ruler. If, for instance, we wish to find the center of a segment 1-2 (113), only the ends of which are given, we draw circles with a radius 1-2 from point 1 and from point 2, and find their intersection 3. Then with the same radius we trace a circle from that point, which gives the point 4. Still with the same radius, we draw another circle (through 3 and 2), which intersects the second circle at 5; from 5 with radius 5-3 and from 1 with radius 1-5, two further circles are drawn which intersect each other at 6 and 7; from these points through 5 we draw two circles whose intersection M is the desired center. The figure has 8 circles. (Can there be fewer?)

Given two intersecting circles, we may find (114A) their centers by means of the ruler alone. We choose point a on one of the circles; through an intersection of the circles and point a we trace a straight line and find point b. Then we return from b through the other intersection to c. Starting from A instead of a, we find in the same manner B and C. We now join a to c and A to C, also A to a and C to c, using dashed lines, and thus obtain the points S and T. The line ST (dotted and dashed) passes through the center of the circle $AaCc$; repeating the construction with another point, we obtain a second diameter and the center. (How many lines are necessary?)

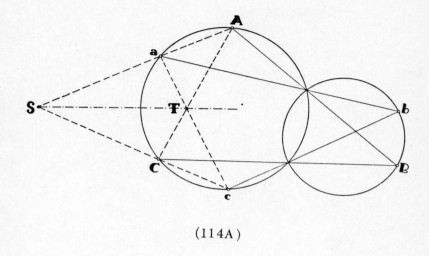

(114A)

If we use only a compass and a ruler, it
is impossible to get a construction that will
give the circumference of a circle, if the
radius is already given. The ratio of the circumference of a circle to its diameter is
3.141592653. . . . Father Kochański, a Polish
Jesuit, gave the following approximate construction (114B): From point A on the
circle we draw another circle with the same
radius and obtain 1; from 1 we trace a circle
with still the same radius, 2; the line joining
2 to the center O intersects the tangent
drawn at A in point 3. By measuring off a
triple radius upon it from point 3, we get 6,
and the segment $B6$ is approximately equal
to one half of the circumference. (With
what approximation?)

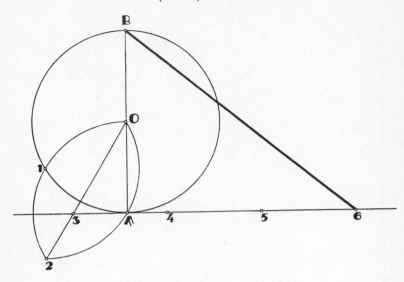

(114B)

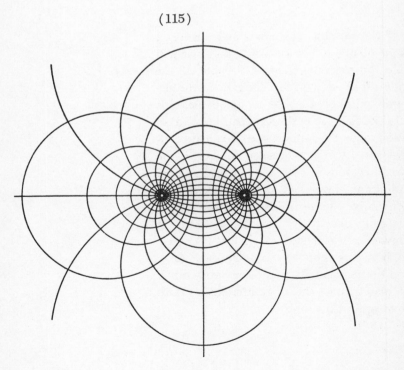

(115)

If we draw all possible circles through two points (115), there exists a second series of circles meeting them at right angles. This second series consists of Apollonius' circles (cf. Fig. 99). Three domains of arbitrary shape and situation being given (116), it is always possible to halve them all by a circle. To halve two domains a straight line is sufficient. The corresponding property in space is the 'sandwich theorem': it is always possible to cut a sandwich with a plane stroke so as to halve the bread, the butter, and the ham.

(116)

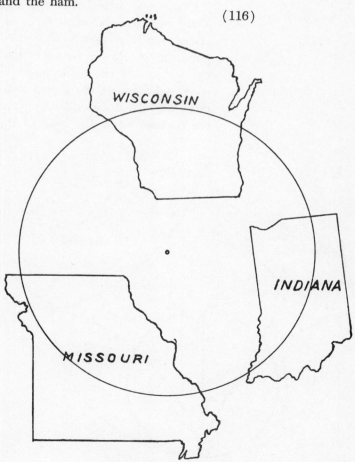

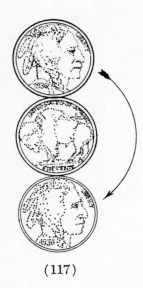

(117)

If we roll one coin along another of the same size (117), the point of contact will run along the circumferences of both the moving and the fixed coin. The circumferences are obviously equal; hence if the point passes along half of the circumference of the fixed coin, it will pass half the circumference of the moving coin. But on testing this system, we find that the moving coin again lies heads up. (Why?)

Copernicus states that if a circle rolls along the internal circumference of another circle whose diameter is twice as long, each point on the circumference of the smaller circle describes a straight line (118A). Let us consider a match fixed as a chord to the small circle and watch its movement from the moment when the head of the match

(118A)

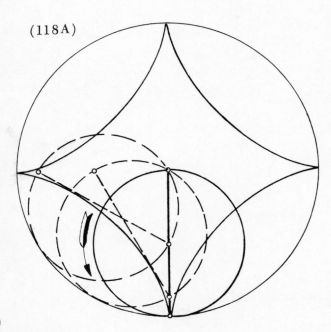

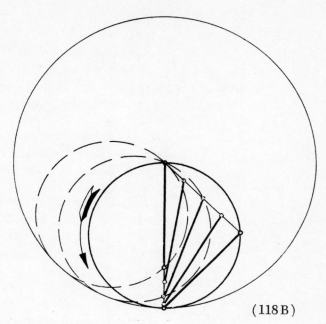

(118 B)

touches the large circle till the moment
when the other end reaches the center of
the large circle. The match has swept the
area of a right triangle, and every point of
this area has been touched only once by the
match. Conversely, if we move a match so
that both ends of it travel on intersecting
straight lines, the movement can be obtained by the Copernican system of rolling
a circle in another twice as great. The
center of the large circle lies at the point of
intersection of the given straight lines, and
the small circle is given by the ends of the
match and the center of the large circle. It
passes through these three points (and
keeps passing through them during the
whole movement) (118B). This experiment fails when the match equals the diameter of the small circle; it then sweeps out
the interior of an asteroid.

When a wheel rolls along a straight line (119), a point marked on its circumference (nail P) describes a *cycloid*. At every moment, each point of the circumference moves toward the highest point or away from it, the speed being proportional to the distance of the moving point from the lowest point. Let us suppose another circle, twice as great, rolling with the same speed as the given circle, and let us mark its diameter, which was vertical at the start: it always touches the cycloid beneath, gliding on it. By fixing the point nearer the center, we obtain a (120) curve without cusps, and when we fix it upon the prolongation of the radius, we get (121) a looped curve. The length of the arc of a cycloid is equal to the circumference of a square circumscribed

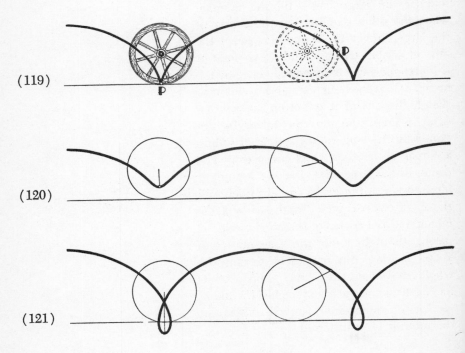

(119)

(120)

(121)

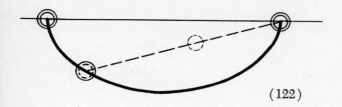

(122)

about the rolling circle. Let us turn Figure 119 upside down; then the point P, if it were a heavy ball and the cycloid a groove, would slide down at the same rate as if an invisible generating circle traveled with a uniform, rolling motion along the horizontal road above, with the ball attached to its circumference. A ball falling along a cycloidal groove (122) anticipates one falling along the inclined plane, even when it must return upwards. Our sketch shows an inclined plane (dashed line); and shows also the position of the ball on the plane at the moment when the ball moving along the cycloid crosses the plane. Such calculations are greatly facilitated by the fact, remarked by Kant, that points falling along inclined planes and starting from the same spot (123) simultaneously form a circular arrangement at any time. The ball falling along the cycloidal groove reaches its goal faster than along any other curved groove.

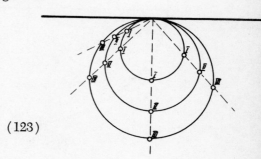

(123)

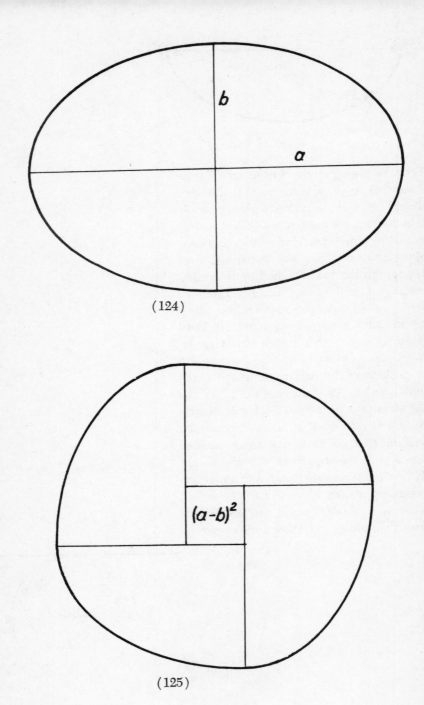

(124)

(125)

124

A circle has the largest area of all curved lines of the same circumference. Hence the area of a field, enclosed by a curved line of the length L, is never greater than $L^2/4\pi$. (Why?) The area enclosed by curves different from a circle can always be augmented without changing their length; if a curve has two rectangular axes of symmetry (124) this can be shown by cutting the area along the axes and putting the four parts together again (125), after having turned two of them upside down. The square in the middle shows the increase of the area, the length is obviously the same as before.

(126)

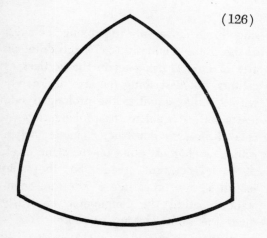

A circle has constant breadth: we can roll a round disc upon the table without the hand rising or falling. But there are other curves of constant breadth. If we draw circles around the vertices of an equilateral triangle as centers with radii equal to its sides, we get also (126) a curved line of constant breadth; if we wish to have it

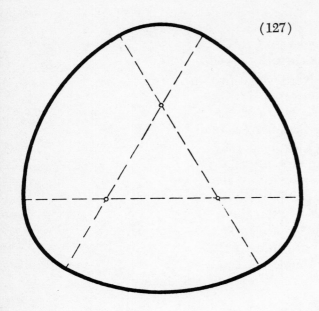

(127)

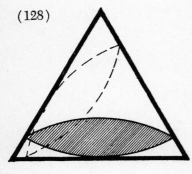

(128)

smooth, we have only to prolong the sides of the triangle equally (127) and draw six arcs of circles, using again the vertices as centers, but describing the arcs alternately with a radius equal to the prolonged side and a radius equal to the prolongation. A curved line so constructed keeps, when rolling, its highest point on the same level. A line of constant breadth has the same length as any other line of the same constant breadth; the longimeter obviously gives the same measure in both cases — which can be considered as a proof. The length is equal to breadth times 3.14159.... (Why?) A circle can roll in the interior of a triangle, touching always all sides. In the case of an equilateral triangle the smallest area having this property is a lens-shaped figure (128) enclosed by two congruent arcs of a circle whose radius is the height of the triangle.

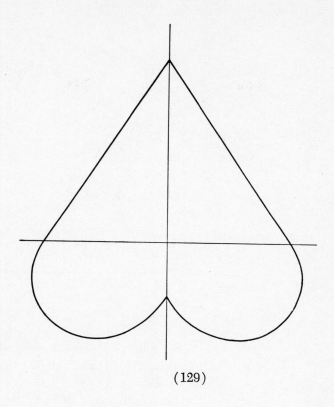

(129)

A circle has the property that a rod of a homogeneous material lighter than water, of circular section, may float motionless on water, no matter how we turn it round the axis. The contours given here (129), (130), have the same property, if we assume the density of the material of the rod to be 1/2; they are so calculated that every chord that halves the circumference also halves the area. Hence this property is not peculiar to the circle. The second curved line of the same property is seen to have three axes of symmetry and three straight segments as parts of its contour.

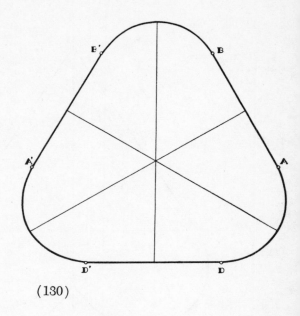

(130)

Some soldiers have been ordered to start from point P (131) and halt 30 paces behind the trench. Each of them chose a different direction, and, upon halting, they formed a bent line, the so-called *conchoid of Nicomedes*. Afterward they were commanded to return 60 paces, then 30 paces more, then 30 paces again. Thus a second line was formed (the full line on the sketch), a third with a cusp, and a fourth with a loop; the dotted lines indicate where the soldiers found themselves after executing the first and last maneuvers.

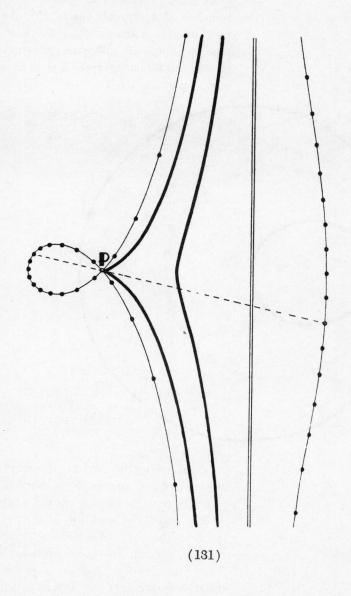

(131)

A similar experiment with a circular trench leads to *Pascal's snail.* (132) In this case the lines arising after the first and second command (30 paces beyond the trench and 60 back) make a single smooth curve, crossing itself.

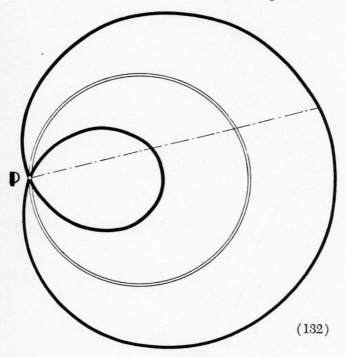

(132)

Of all curves the circle is the most symmetrical: it has an infinite number of axes of symmetry. To get a symmetrical replica of any object we can use a mirror. The mirror is the plane of symmetry. Placing a circular disc in space, let us consider its image in a mirror and let a plane pass through the centers of the real and imaginary discs so as to cut out of them the diameters maximally inclined toward the mirror. By joining (133) the endpoints of these diameters crosswise, we find a point on the mirror. If we make this point a vertex of a cone having the real circle as its base, we shall see another cone in the mirror. Both cones can be considered as one, because the generating lines of the real cone give, when prolonged, the generating lines of the imaginary one. Thus we get the construction of our photograph; the mirror has been abolished. The straight line, however, which joins the center of one disc to the vertex of the cone, does not pass through the center of the second disc, as the black wire of our model clearly indicates. (It is easy to verify this statement by cutting the model by the auxiliary plane mentioned above and by reducing it to an obvious fact of plane geometry; the figure obtained consists of three wires and two diameters and is visible on our photograph.) (133) This fact proves the impossibility of constructing the center of a circle by using only a ruler. For if such construction were possible, we could, by drawing it on the plane of one circle and projecting it through the vertex of the cone on the plane of the other circle, obtain a second construction, executed strictly according to the same rules, because the straight lines pass into straight lines and their intersections into intersections. This is true also of the intersections of the straight lines with the circle. Hence the center of the first circle, being one of these intersections, should pass into the center of the second circle, but that is not the case. This proof of impossibility is highly characteristic of mathematics.

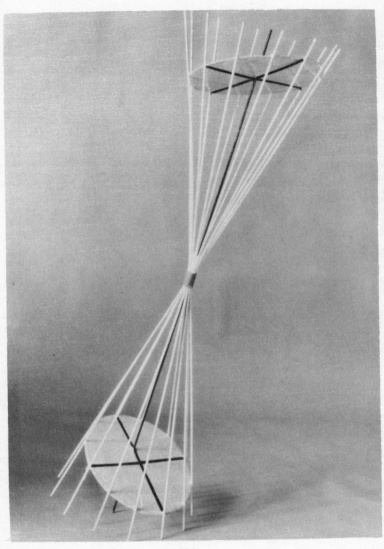

(133)

(134)

To make a plane picture of a three dimensional object, we appeal to *geometrical perspective*. A camera furnishes it automatically but the ancient masters employed the same means to obtain the impression of perspective depth. (134) Horizontal parallels always meet on the 'horizon-line' of the picture; if they are perpendicular to the background, their apex is the 'principal point' (marked here by a small circle). Only by placing the eye on the perpendicular to the picture issuing from the principal point does one get, without deformation, the visual impression corresponding to the three-dimensional reality.

(135)

The optical illusion of a portrait following with its eyes a spectator walking along is easy to explain. In the case of a living immobile model (135) the view changes as we walk along: first one ear disappears behind the head, then one eye begins to hide behind the nose, and so on. Only if the model turns its head to watch us frontally, do we continue to see both ears, both eyes, and so on. Now, with a picture we always see both eyes and both ears, whatever our point of view; thus the portrait makes the impression of a person's turning his head to look at us.

On a summer afternoon the author saw a swarm of little flies dancing, as mosquitoes do, in one place and then flashing quickly to another place some yards away to dance there in pairs and to return after a minute or so to the old place and to repeat the same play again and again. This game lasted long enough to allow him to determine roughly the velocity of the jump; it was about 40 miles per hour. When looking attentively, he could see on the track of the jump (136) sparkles of light; they formed dotted lines and were approximately half an inch apart. It was obviously the effect of the sun shining sideways on the insects; they became visible only when their wings were

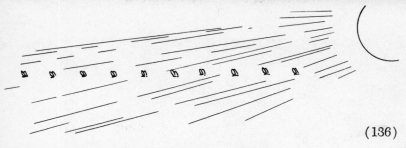

(136)

lifted and illuminated by the sun. Every
rosary of sparkles belonged to one single fly
and their plurality was only an illusion resulting from the permanence of the images
on the retina. Forty miles per hour is about
700 inches which equals 1400 half-inches per
second: it follows that the frequency of
beats of flies' wings was 1400 per second;
allowing 40 per cent for error of estimation,
we can summarize the observation as giving
a thousand or more beats per second. It is
curious that such a computation can be
made without instruments.

The principle of symmetry can be applied
to the following toy. On a board of wood
we place a little ball of steel (137) on a
support (a tube fixed to the board); the ball
is about an inch above the board. Another
support carries a similar brilliant ball a foot
above the board. The same support carries
also a sheet of glass and the distances are
calculated so that the glass is a plane of symmetry for the two balls. Looking from
above the glass, we see the ball beneath
because of the transparency of the glass,
and the ball above because the glass acts
as a mirror. Nevertheless, we see only one
ball; both images are confounded into one
because of the symmetrical position of the
balls. Now let us lay a puppet of clay on
the board, covering the lower ball; when

(137)

looking as before (138), we still see the ball because the reflected image remains. This view is optically equivalent to the view of the lower ball. We can prove it by reaching through the clay with our fingers or with a surgical tool and removing the ball as if it were visible. The idea described here can be used to localize foreign bodies by X-rays, but here the problem is reversed. The hidden object in the patient's body is originally

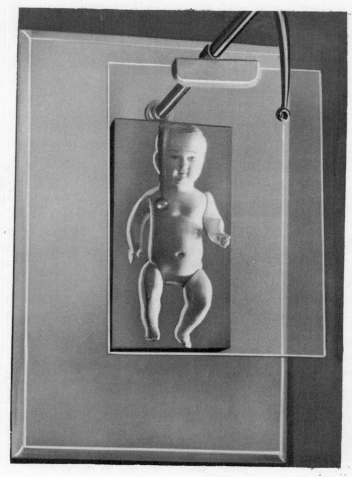

(138)

undetermined, and, by means of screening, the glass and the replica (an electric bulb) are brought to the proper position. Then the X-rays are shut off and the surgeon operates in daylight, exactly as in the toy described above.

Some optical fallacies are of a very startling character. When viewing a fence of wire of the kind in Figure 10, it happens occasionally that we are deceived as to the distance of the fence and we fail to grasp it, reaching too short. To evoke this phenomenon, we look first far behind the fence and then suddenly draw our attention to it. The explanation is that, because all squares of the fence are alike, we have no guide to tell us which of the left-eye images corresponds to a right-eye image. If we identify two images of two different squares crosswise and attribute them to a real square, we locate this square on the crossing of the lines of vision, — which brings the fence closer to us than it really is. It is also possible to push the fence back, but this is more difficult. (Why?) The difference between images of the same object seen with the left and with the right eye is the chief factor for stereoscopic vision. To get pictures that convey the stereoscopic impression, the method of anaglyphs draws suitable sketches in perspective. Anaglyphs are two projections of the real object, one from the center of the left, another from the center of the right pupil. The first is red, the other green-blue; looking at them with two-colored spectacles (red glass for the right eye and green-blue for the left), we shall see a plastic picture. (Why?)

A very simple optical fallacy hinders our estimating the distance of a horizontal wire without visible poles sustaining it. The reason is the homogeneity of the wire. If there were a red spot on it, we should direct both axes of vision on the spot and immediately get the perception of distance; if there is no such mark, it is sufficient to incline the head on one shoulder. (Why?)

Cubes, Spiders, Honeycombs, and Bricks

NATURE realizes cubes in the shape of salt crystals (*NaCl*) (139); we can fill the whole space with them. A cube may be painted in 30 different ways, with six colors, a different one for each face. If we have 30 such models and take any one of them, we can find 8 other cubes and build of them a larger cube in such a way that the colors of the adjoining faces will be the same and that the arrangement of colors on the large cube will be exactly the same as that on the small one.

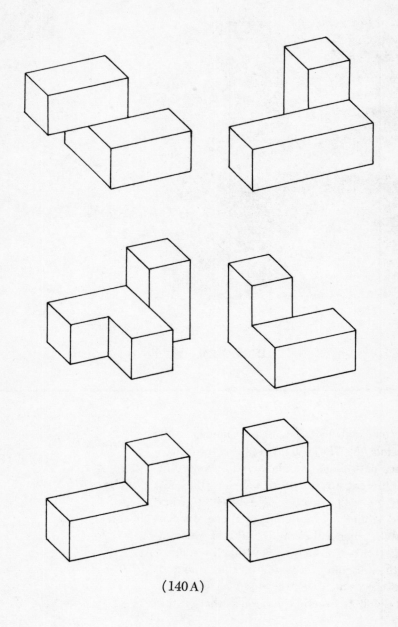

(140 A)

Of these six pieces (140A) we may form a cube (140B), a process that is by no means an easy task. There are two solutions. If the cube's edge is 3 inches, there are among those pieces three composed each of 5 little cubes with one-inch edges, and three composed each of 4 such little cubes. Two pieces are congruent by symmetry (was it possible to avoid it?). By putting the pieces together in the way indicated here (141), we get a beautiful architectural design (142); the number of different designs is almost unlimited.

(140 B)

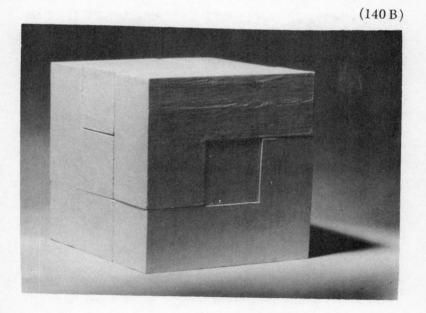

(141)

(142)

142

(143)

A cube intersected by a plane halving the long diagonal and perpendicular to it gives for section (143) a regular hexagon. We also get a regular hexagon when we view from above a cube whose long diagonal is perpendicular to the (144) horizontal plane of projection.

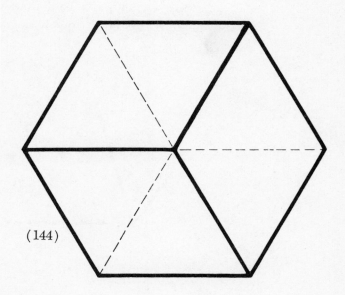

(144)

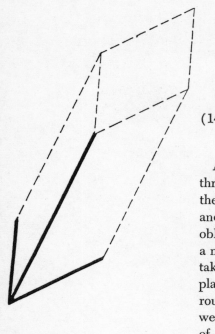

(145)

According to Pohlke, one may draw any three segments from one point, complete the figure with (dashed) parallel segments, and (145), (146) consider it as a (generally oblique) projection of a cube. If we make a model cube of white wire (147) and then take several photographs of it on the same plate, turning it before taking each view, round the large diagonal by the same angle, we shall obtain a picture (148) composed of two cones and a hyperboloid of revolution. (The photograph shows clearly the hyperbola that is the meridian of that hyperboloid.) The hyperboloid is a surface composed of two families of straight lines.

The straight line is the shortest path. We can make use of this rule to determine the

(146)

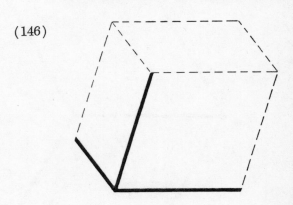

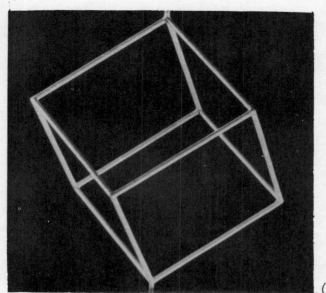

(147)

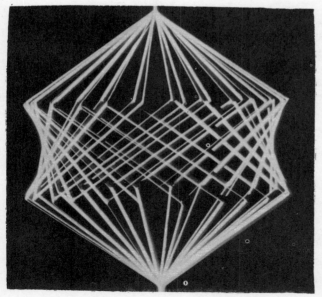

(148)

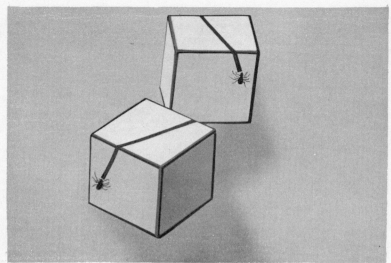

(149)

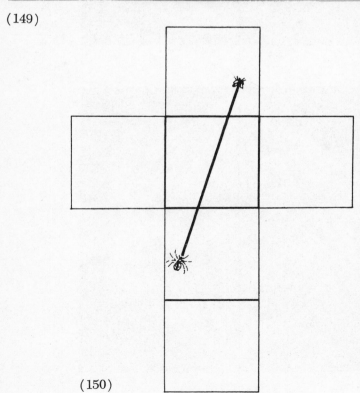

(150)

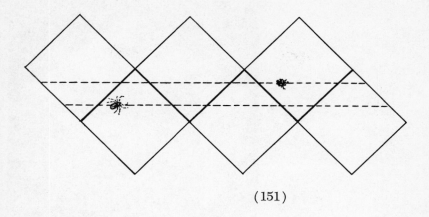

shortest route on a cube. When a spider
sitting on the cube (149) wants to catch a
fly sitting on another face, it will find the
shortest way in the shape of a straight line
upon the diagram (150) of the cube. If the
fly wishes to make sure that there is no
spider on the cube and, leaving its position,
wants to crawl over all the faces of the cube
and return as quickly as possible, its route
on the diagram (151) will also be a straight
line. It is likewise apparent from the diagram that the point of departure does not
affect the length of the circuit (152). The
fly has, however, the choice of two different
ways. The shortest circuits cover the whole
cube with lines (hexagons) of constant
length, two such lines passing through every
point. Would it be possible to make one
family of these lines of white thread and
another of red thread, so as to get on each
face of the cube a two-colored fabric, the
threads of the same color being parallel?
No, four colors are necessary. (Why?)

(152)

To find shortest paths we can sometimes proceed as with the cube: spread the surface, on which the path is to be traced, on a plane, draw a straight line, and bend the model back to its previous shape. For instance, a cone is a surface woven of a group of straight lines. A fly, wishing to take a turn round the cone and get back to where it was as soon as possible, would follow the loop (153) that returns to the starting point at an angle. The cone, cut along one of the straight lines (154) and laid open, would present a sector, and the fly's route would consist of two lines perpendicular to the sides of the sector. If the cone is equilateral or even more blunted, the solution is a different one: the fly walks straight to the top, takes a look round, and comes back the same way.

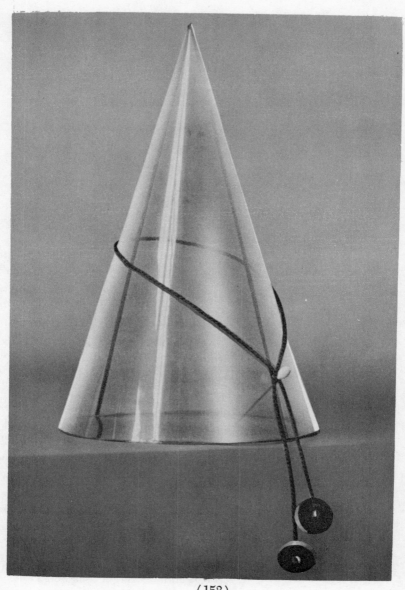

(153)

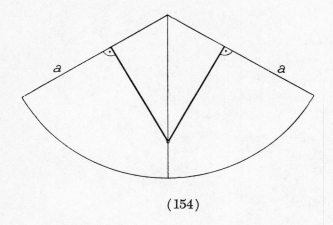

(154)

There are surfaces that cannot be spread out as the cone; the sphere is such a surface. The shortest lines on the sphere are the great circles, the socalled *orthodromes;* every meridian is such an orthodrome. Let us suppose we could spread out, without stretching, the sphere's surface on a plane. All the orthodromes would conserve their lengths and become shortest ways on the plane, and thus they would become straight lines. On the other hand they are closed, while straight lines are not. This fact shows the impossibility of spreading the whole sphere on the plane. But even when we try to spread a part of the sphere, the part of the earth's surface that lies north of the polar circle, for instance, we encounter an absurdity: the meridians converging in the North Pole (155), (156) become, when spread out, straight segments of equal length and the whole cap becomes a disc whose boundary is a circle. This circle is the polar circle, which conserves its length too;

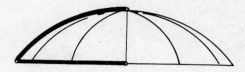

the radius of this circle is equal to the radius of the polar circle — which is to be seen on the plane cutting the sphere in the polar circle, whereas the distance from the North Pole measured along the meridian (drawn as a heavy bent line on the sketch) is obviously greater. The radius of the cap when spread out must therefore be equal to two different segments at the same time — which is absurd.

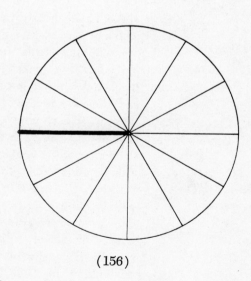

(156)

(157)

We have already mentioned filling the
whole of space with cubes. We can get another filling of this sort by the following
procedure: we make the cubes alternately
black and white to get a kind of chessboard
and then we remove the black ones. We
decompose each void space into 6 pyramids
on square bases with a common vertex in
the center of the void space. If we consider
a single white cube (157) with six pyramids
based on it, we see a rhombic dodecahedron
with a cube inscribed in it; it is obvious
that by our procedure we have filled the
whole of space (158) with congruent
rhombic dodecahedra. It is very easy to find
the volume of such a dodecahedron: we

have used two cubes to build up one dodecahedron, and it has therefore twice the volume of the cube, $2a^3$, if a is the edge of the cube. The shorter diagonal of the rhombic faces is a, the longer one $a\sqrt{2}$, thus the sides of the rhombs are $b = a\sqrt{3}$, and the volume $2a^3$ of the solid equals $2b^3/3\sqrt{3}$. The vertices are of two kinds: (1) where 4 solids meet; (2) where 6 solids meet.

(158)

The cells in a honeycomb can be obtained from two layers of dodecahedra by replacing the free faces (3 in every dodecahedron) by a hexagonal aperture (159); thus, there are in every honeycomb points where 4 and points where 6 cells meet.

(159)

There is an interesting question involved
in filling the space with congruent polyhedra so as to have only 4 meeting in every
vertex (it is impossible to have only 3). To
find such polyhedra, let us consider the
bricks in a wall extending indefinitely in all
directions. When laying the first layer, we
shall stick to the mason's thumb rule to
block interstices by adjoining bricks (160).

We notice that the first layer (full lines on the sketch) is not an essentially new tessellation of the plane; if we consider every point where three bricks meet as a vertex, we see that every region is a hexagon, and the whole only a distortion of the honeycomb pattern of Figure 54. Laying a similar layer on the first (dashed lines), we want to cover every vertex by a brick. Thus we get four bricks meeting at every vertex. Laying a third layer on the second, we place it exactly over the first and repeat the procedure indefinitely. Let us count how many neighbors each brick (161) has. There are 6 in the same layer, 4 above, and 4 beneath it, a total of 14. Let us imagine the neighbors' edges painted black and gradually decompose our masonry (162), (163) to see on the white brick the black traces left by the edges of adjoining bricks. We see 14 domains, left by 14 neighbors. Thus the brick is a 14-hedron, squeezed to the shape of an ordinary brick. To find the undistorted shape, let us remark that we find on the brick 6 'squares' and 8 'hexagons.'

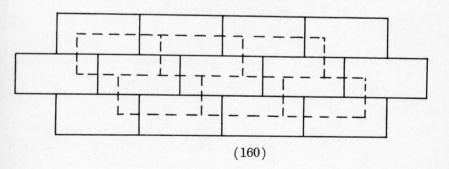

(160)

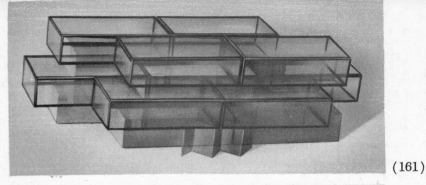

(161)

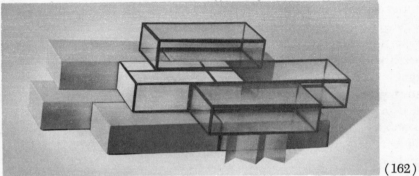

(162)

(163)

This observation leads to the truncated octahedron (164). It is our distorted brick and fills the whole space (165) in such a way that only 4 solids meet in each vertex; it is semiregular, — which means that its faces are regular polygons. There is no other solid having these properties and thus it gives the simplest decomposition of space in congruent parts.

(164)

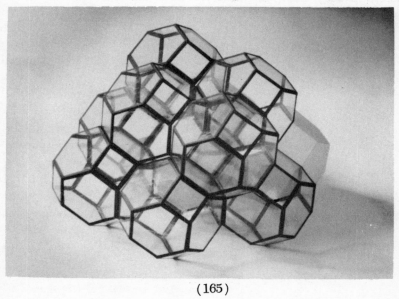

(165)

(166)

Platonic Solids, Crystals, Bees' Heads, and Soap

PLATO knew that there were only five regular polyhedra. How can four triangles be made from six matches? To do it, it is necessary to make a basic triangle with three of the matches, and with the remainder form the three edges of a pyramid. Thus arises (166) a regular tetrahedron, the first of the Platonic polyhedra. It looks like this (167) when projected vertically on its base. Another projection can give a square with diagonals (168) and the model can be obtained from a flat diagram. (169) The second Platonic body, the cube, has already been shown.

From eight equilateral triangles (170) it is possible to compose the third Platonic

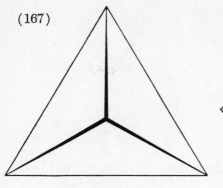

(167)

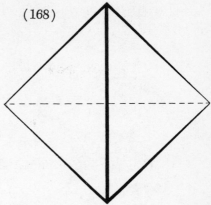

(168)

body, the regular octahedron. By placing it on one of the triangular faces and projecting it on the plane of the base, we obtain the drawing (171), which shows (thick dashed lines) that the centers of the faces of the octahedron (172) are also vertices of a cube. Conversely, the centers of the faces of the cube (173) are vertices of an octahedron.

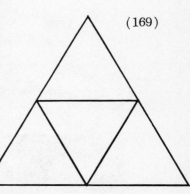

(169)

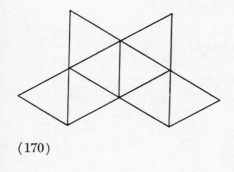

(170)

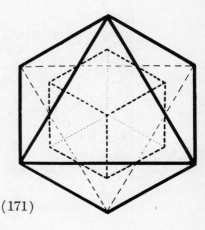

(171)

(172)

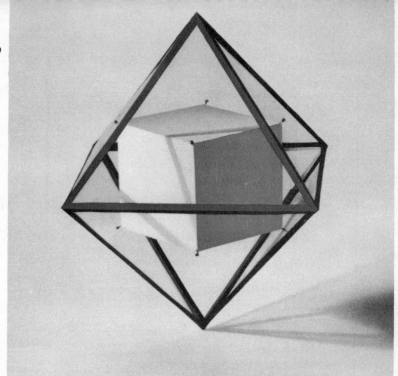

(173)

The following Platonic solid, a regular dodecahedron (174), has pentagonal faces. From the diagram (175) we may easily obtain a model. We have to pass the point of a knife along the edges (on the side of the cardboard that has to become the exterior of the model); then we place one star crosswise on another (176) and bind them by passing an elastic thread alternately above and beneath the corners of the double star, holding the model flat with the other hand. Removing the hand (177), we see the dodecahedron rising (178) as a perfect model. To paint its faces so that adjoining faces have different colors, no less than four colors are sufficient. These colors being

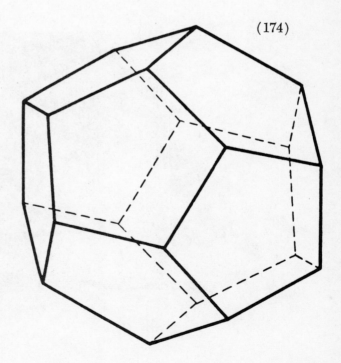

(174)

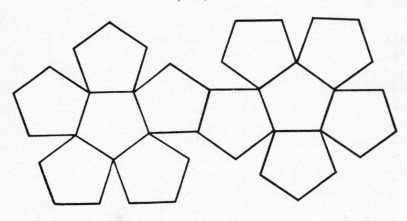

(177)

(178)

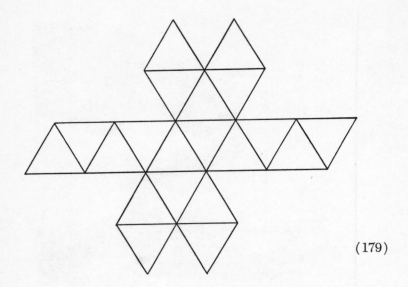

(179)

given, there are only two ways of distribut-
ing them on the dodecahedron, if we consider an arrangement of colors as identical
with any other that is to be obtained from
the first by a rotation of the model. Of the
two essentially different paintings existing,
one is a symmetrical image of the other, i.e.
one model gives both arrangements if we
hold it opposite a mirror.

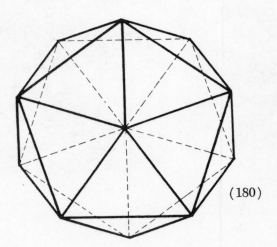

(180)

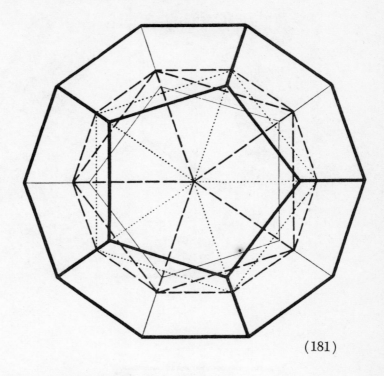

(181)

The last of the regular solids is an icosahedron. Its diagram (179) is composed of twenty equilateral triangles. Its horizontal projection (180) can be combined with that of the dodecahedron (181); in fact the centers of the faces (182) of the dodecahedron form the vertices of the icosahedron, as our model proves. Conversely, the centers of the faces of the icosahedron form the vertices of the dodecahedron (183), (184). Only the tetrahedron corresponds to itself, as the centers of its faces (185) are the vertices of another tetrahedron.

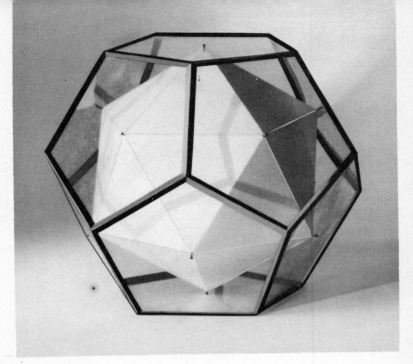

(182)

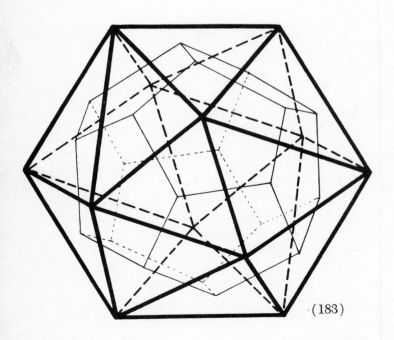

(183)

(184)

(185)

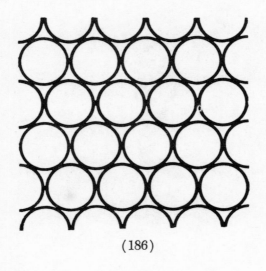

(186)

Balls of equal size do not fill a space.
The same principle applies to circles in the
plane (186): their densest possible distribution reminds us of the honeycomb and
we can well imagine how the circles when
squeezed would become hexagons. The
densest arrangement of spheres can be obtained by dividing the whole of space in
cubic cells (without walls but with edges
of wire) by calling them alternately black
and white and placing in every white cell
a sphere as large as possible. Thus only half
of the cells will carry spheres and it will be
easy to compute the ratio of the part of
space occupied by spheres to the whole
space. There is one sphere for each pair of
cubes; the cube's edge being a, the radius

of a sphere is half the diagonal of the square a^2, that is to say $a\sqrt{2}/2$. The volume of the sphere will be therefore

$$4/3 \cdot \pi \cdot (a\sqrt{2}/2)^3$$

and the volume of the pair of cubes being $2a^3$, the ratio is $\pi\sqrt{2}/6 = 0.7403$. Thus the densest arrangement of spheres occupies about 74 per cent of the whole space. Thus, if we have a soap mixed with gasoline, the soap's proportion being more than 75 per cent, we are sure that the gasoline cannot form a medium in which the soap is suspended in little spheres; we know that it is the gasoline that is suspended in the soap. Thus the emulsion will not be inflammable and its domestic use involves no danger.

There is another way leading to the densest arrangement of spheres. We place first a layer of balls on the plane in such a manner that viewed from above, they look like Figure 186. Now we place a similar layer on the first, putting each ball of the upper layer into a hollow formed by three balls beneath it. Notice that balls cannot be placed in three adjoining hollows. Therefore if we place now a third layer upon the second, we may do so in such a way that its balls come to lie over the hollows of the first layer, left free by the second layer (187), we may also dispose them otherwise (188), viz. so that its balls lie over the balls of the first layer. In both cases each ball of the middle layer is in contact with 12 neighbors. In the first method these points of contact are vertices of a cuboctahedron,

(187)

(188)

(189)

(190

the crystal of argentite (Ag_2S) (189), which arises by cutting off the vertices of a regular octahedron by a cube whose faces halve the octahedron's edges. In the second method they give the vertices of another 14-hedron (190) composed, like the first, of 6 squares and 8 equilateral triangles. If we halve it by passing a plane through the edges forming a hexagon, turn one half against the other 60°, and join the halves again, we obtain the cuboctahedron.

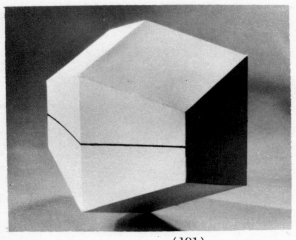

(191)

Now let us suppose that the balls are of yeast and that they rise equally. The gaps between them will fill up, and each ball will be transformed into a polyhedron whose faces will be found to be the common tangent planes of the balls. In the first case we shall get the rhombic dodecahedra of Figures 157 and 158, and in the second, solids (191) limited by 6 rhombi and 6 trapezoids. We can obtain the first solid from the second by cutting it along the equator and by turning the upper half 60° round a vertical axis. In this way we find both solids having the same volume, the same surface, and vertices of the same kind, while their faces have the same circumferences, the same areas, and the same angles. The first method of placing spheres shows also that the cuboctahedron can be inscribed into the rhombic dodecahedron; the second method gives an analogous result. (Which?)

We have already seen how space can be filled with rhombic dodecahedra; it can be filled with the other dodecahedra, as the experiment with yeast explains. The cells of a honeycomb can be obtained by squeezing two layers of balls placed upon each other in the densest way. We thus obtain two layers of hexagonal, angular columns ending with trirhombic roofs; the roofs of one layer will be also those of the second. We might account for the origin of honeycombs by the action of elastic balls (in this case the bees' heads packed as densely as possible upon both sides of a thin wax slab).

The fluorite crystal ($CaFe_2$) (192) resembles the truncated octahedron, our distorted brick of Figure 164. The crystal of pyrite (FeS_2) resembles a regular dodecahedron (193A), whereas other minerals crystallize in very interesting irregular forms: the sphalerite (ZnS) whose crystals

(192)

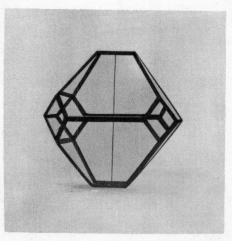

(193 A)

(193B)

174

(194)

are dodecahedra limited by congruent deltoids (193B), or the cuprite (Cu_2O) which takes the shape of trisoctahedra (24-hedra) bounded by congruent irregular (194) pentagons. If we place a plane along each edge of a regular dodecahedron, perpendicular to the plane of symmetry in which this edge lies, we shall obtain (195) a rhombic triacontahedron. The diagonals of the rhombic faces are the edges of regular polyhedra: the shorter ones give a dodecahedron, the longer edges an icosahedron. Proceeding with the triacontahedron as before with the dodecahedron, we get a 60-hedron. (What faces will it have?)

(195)

The problem of proportional polling solved in the plane for three political parties (Fig. 52) leads, in the case of four parties, to a division of a regular tetrahedron by means of planes parallel to its faces and equally distant from each other (196). Employing an infinite number of planes in each of the four families of equidistant parallel planes, we get a filling of the whole space. It is a filling composed of regular tetrahedra and regular octahedra.

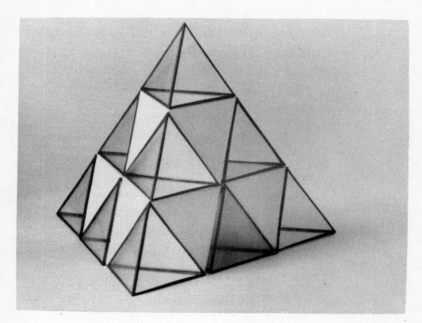

(196)

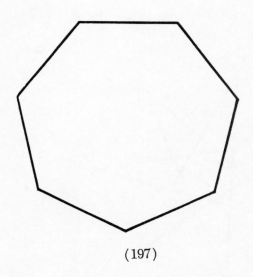

(197)

(198 A)

(198 B)

(198 C)

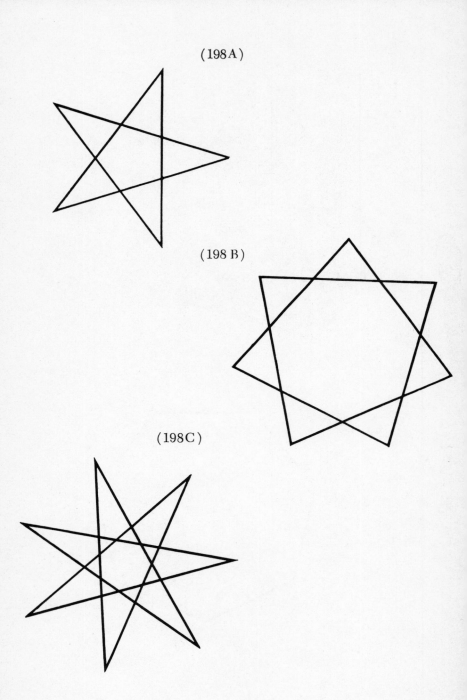

In addition to ordinary polygons we find
the so-called 'stellated' forms (197, 198A,
B, C). The stellated pentagon, the 'penta-
gramma mysticum,' is the favorite figure of
magicians and astrologers. There are three
heptagons, one convex and two stellated.
This photograph (199) gives an idea of a
polyhedron bounded by 12 stellated pentagons.

We can choose four vertices of a cube to be vertices of a regular tetrahedron. This can be done in two ways (200) and the two tetrahedra together give a 'stellated octahedron.'

(200)

Soap-Bubbles, Earth and Moon, Maps, and Dates

THE easiest way to obtain a sphere is by blowing a soap bubble. The surface of the liquid film tends to diminish the surface of that film. The bubble encloses a certain quantity of air, hence the film assumes the form of a surface that, the volume being given, has the smallest possible area; the sphere is the only surface with this property (201). The moon was once a liquid ball; as every drop of the fluid attracted every other drop of the fluid mass, the drops arranged themselves in such a way that every change in the shape would require work. It can be proved that only the spherical shape has this property (202A, B).

(202 A, B)

If we take a pipe with two circular openings (203) and dip them in soap suds, we see, when we blow air in the pipe, two caps of film growing equally until they reach the shape of hemispheres. Then a strange thing occurs: one of them continues growing while the other one diminishes. The reason is the property of the sphere being the least area enclosing a given volume. After a certain amount of air has been blown into the pipe, the problem to be solved by nature is to enclose the surplus of air that exceeds the volume of the pipe's tube in as small an area as possible, with the condition that both bubbles are attached to the

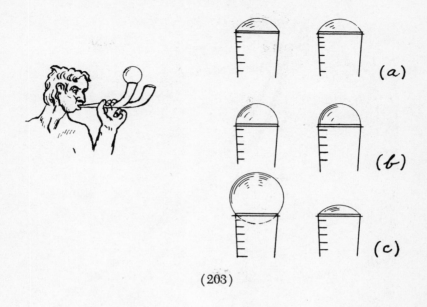

(203)

circular edges. The problem is the same as to enclose a given volume in a surface that has a part above the circular opening and another beneath it, because we can always put the two bubbles together without altering the volume and the area. As long as the amount of air is too small to fill a sphere with the pipe's mouth as equator, the solution is a symmetrical lens. This lens grows to a sphere, and from that moment there exists always a sphere, reposing on the pipe mouth, large enough for any given amount of air. Such a sphere is visible on our sketch with its lower part marked by a dashed arc; when we bring this part back to the other opening, we see why the second bubble decreases. (How?)

(204)

The earth has the shape of a sphere
(204). One of the black lines joining Lisbon
to Cape Farewell (the higher, i.e. the more
northerly one) represents the shortest route
between the two places. It is a great circle
on the sphere, a so-called orthodrome (the
meridians are also orthodromes; of the parallels of latitude only the Equator is an

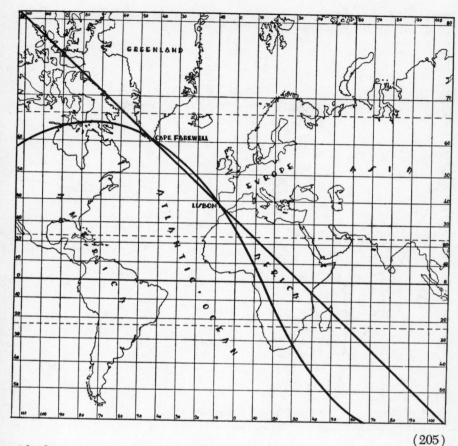

(205)

orthodrome). The second line is a loxodrome, i. e. a line representing a fixed
course; it intersects all the meridians at the
same angle. A sailor who has chosen a direction on the compass and keeps it steadily
is following a loxodrome. The navigation
becomes thereby much easier, but the
voyage is longer. We see that the loxodrome, when prolonged, coils around the
Pole spirally and would be impracticable
for an explorer of far northern waters.
Mercator's projection (205) is a map that
renders angles accurately; the meridians

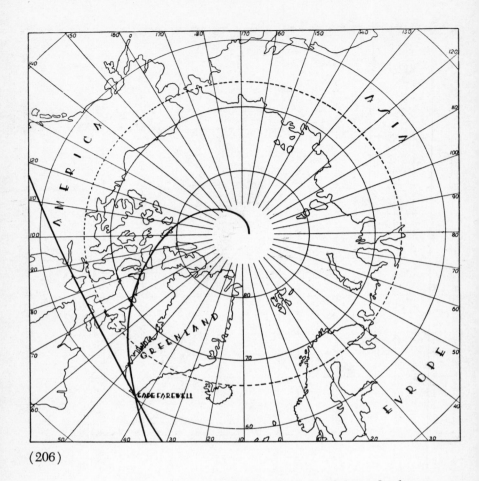

(206)

and the parallels of latitude form a rectangular lattice on the map, and the loxodrome is a straight line. It cuts all meridians on the earth at the same angle and must therefore do the same on the map. The meridians being parallel on the map, the loxodrome cuts parallel lines on the map at a constant angle; it must consequently be a straight line. The orthodrome, on the contrary, shows here an inflexion like a sinusoid (cf. Fig. 221). If we project the surface of the sphere from the South Pole upon a

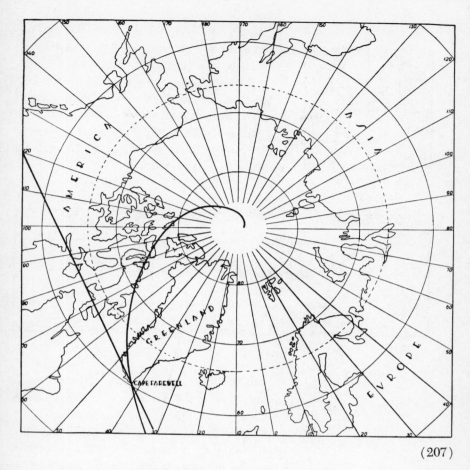

(207)

plane tangent at the North Pole (stereo-
graphic projection), we obtain a map that
represents circles on the globe as circles
and preserves angles (206). Thus on this
map the orthodrome appears as a circle
(with a large radius) and the loxodrome as
a logarithmic spiral. The last proposition
results from the fact that on the map the
meridians are evidently straight lines meeting at the Pole, and that the loxodrome is a
line that cuts all of them at the same angle.
If we projected the globe upon a plane

187

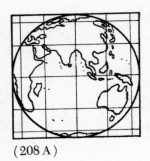

(208 A)

tangent at New York from the antipodes of New York, the meridians and parallels of latitude would give Figure 115.

If we project a sphere upon a plane tangent at the North Pole from the center of the sphere (gnomonic projection), the orthodrome (207) will appear as a straight line. Hence it is the most suitable map for flying in polar regions.

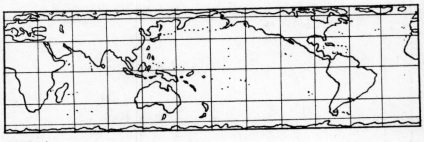

(208 B)

If we place a sphere in a cylinder touching it along the Equator, and if we project the sphere on the cylindrical surface by prolonging the planes of every parallel (208A, B) to cut the cylinder and do the same with all the meridian planes, we get on the cylinder a map of the sphere. By cutting the cylinder open and laying it flat, we get a map of the sphere with a rectangular and a straight net of meridians and parallels. This map has the peculiarity (known already to Archimedes) of conserving areas. If we imagine the sphere covered with a thin uniform layer of paint or clay and bring every particle of it to its proper place on the cylinder, we shall get a uniform covering of the cylinder with matter; if we transfer it horizontally back to the common axis

of the cylinder and the sphere, we shall
cover the axis uniformly with matter. We
could have covered it immediately, without
the mediation of the cylinder. We can,
however, do the same thing differently in
two steps: first we project the matter horizontally by a parallel projection, all par-
ticles falling freely down or going up on the
Equatorial plane (209A), and we get a
spherical distribution (209B); then we project it again on a diameter of the Equator,
getting of course a uniform distribution
(209C). Thus we have found a distribution

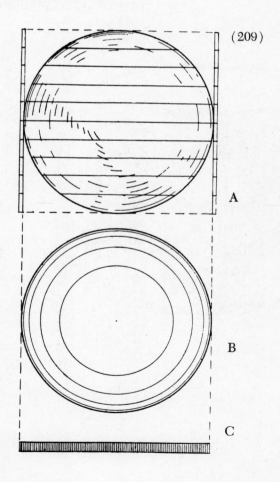

(209)

A

B

C

of matter on a disc that gives a uniform distribution when projected on any diameter of the disc. There is only one solution to this problem.

To explain the paradox of date on our globe, we can imagine the map (208B) to be drawn on a transparent sheet and brought back to cylindric shape by being glued to a drum. One of the meridians separating Asia from America and passing through the Pacific may be used as the date line (210). The time is shown in the form of a ribbon of

(210)

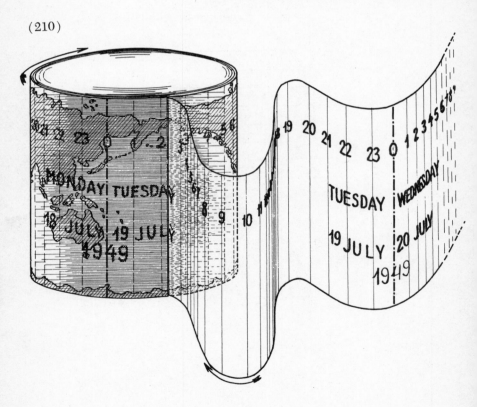

paper drawn by a hidden cylinder of wood rotating inside the immobile Earth; the ribbon crosses the transparent surface of the model through a fissure cut along the date line. The exterior part of the ribbon is the future, the coils already hidden are the past, and the part visible through the transparent map is the 'today.' Thus the ribbon is a sort of calendar carrying days, months, and years; they are separated by transversal lines and divided into hours. As the date changes at midnight and the midnights are transversal lines on the ribbon separating the days, we always see on the Earth two lines of date: the fixed one and the midnight line. Thus we see here Tuesday extending from the fixed line to the mobile one that is West of the fixed line; beyond it, it is still Monday, extending westward from the mobile line back to the fixed line. As the mobile line wanders to the West, Tuesday increases in area and Monday decreases; finally there is a moment when Tuesday reigns the world over. But it lasts only a moment, because Wednesday comes and the midnight line leaves the fixed line of date, moving to the West and creating between itself and the line of date a narrow strip for the new day; Tuesday's decline begins and the play goes on and on.

(211)

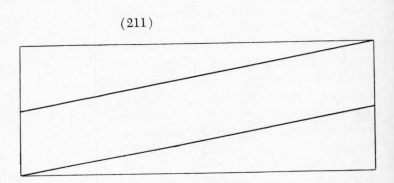

Squirrels, Screws, Candles, Tunes, and Shadows

IT is amusing to watch squirrels running after each other round a tree; their paths are helices. In fact, to find the shortest way on a cylinder, we can cut it along a straight line (211) and lay it out flat (as in the map 208). The shortest route between any two points will give on the picture a straight line; this line, when rolled up back together with the cylinder, changes into a helix (212). The projection of a screw (213) shows cusps at certain points. It is a property of every skew line that we may obtain

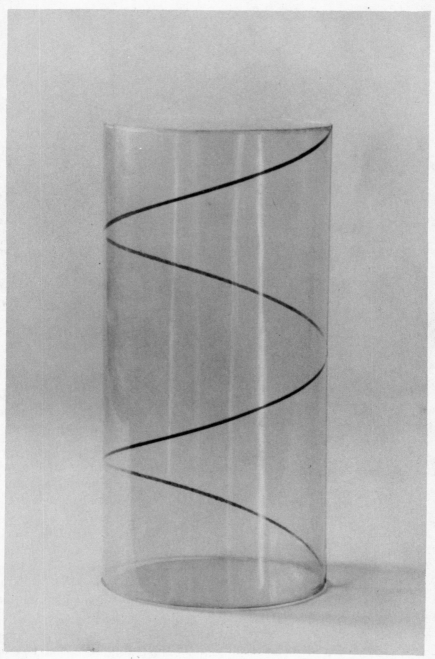

(212)

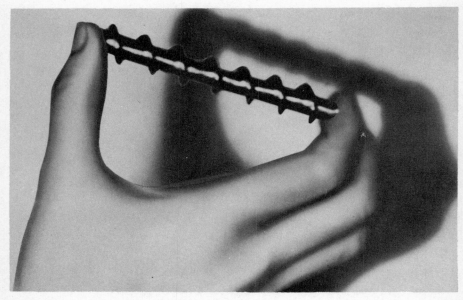

(213)

from any of its points (214) such cusps by an appropriate projection. An ordinary screw has a helix as its edge line. The so-called 'endless' screw (215) changes uniform rotating motion into a uniform progressive motion. If a segment of a given length glides with one end on a helix, its other end gliding along the axis, a helicoidal (216) surface arises. This surface can be obtained by uniformly turning an arm round a rod and by moving the rod uniformly in its own direction at the same time. This surface is the only non-rotary surface capable of gliding on itself. The sphere, the cylinder, and the plane are rotary surfaces; not only can they glide on themselves but they may be so slid over themselves that an arbitrary point will travel on any given track. Hence these four surfaces will always play a dominant part in the structure of machines.

(214)

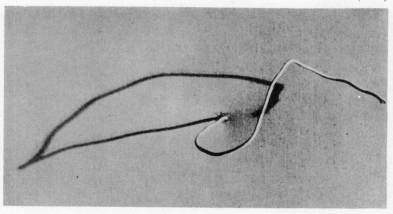

(215)

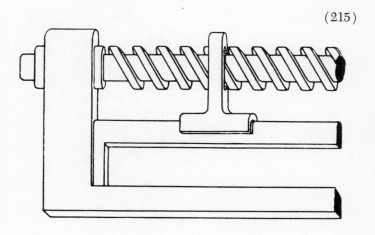

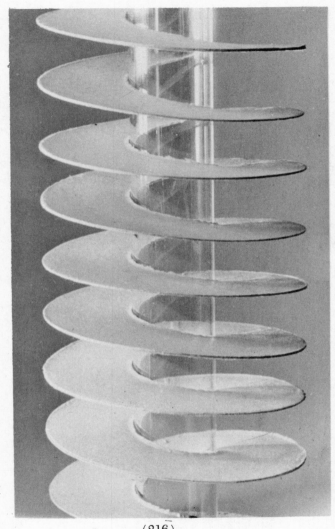

(216)

(217)

When we cut a cylinder by a plane, we get an ellipse (217). It would be erroneous to consider the ellipse a shortest path on the cylinder because of its lying in one plane. If we wind paper round a candle (218), then cut it obliquely (219) with a sharp knife (220), and then unwind the paper (221), we obtain a sinusoid. By adding sinusoids, we can obtain any curve. The lines drawn on the cylinder of a gramophone by the needle when recording a pure note become sinusoids when laid out flat. Here are three sinusoids (222) of equal amplitudes, i.e. equally high; they correspond to the three components of the concord high $C:G:C$. The heavy line is the sum of three sinusoids; it is the curve recorded on the gramophone by the concord. But the same chord gives in different circumstances another (223) line. It is to be seen on our sketch that in the second case the vibrations

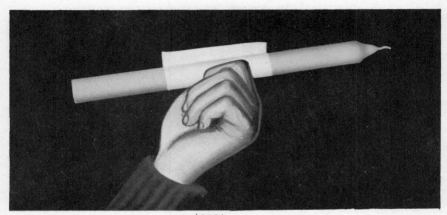

(218)

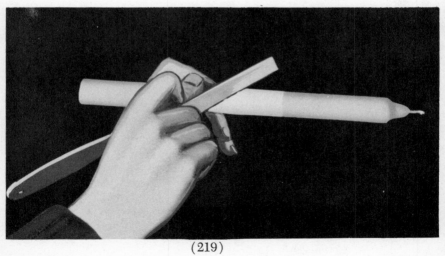

(219)

198

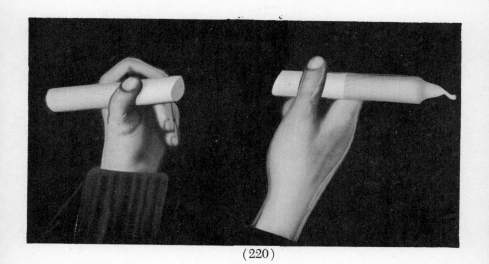

(220)

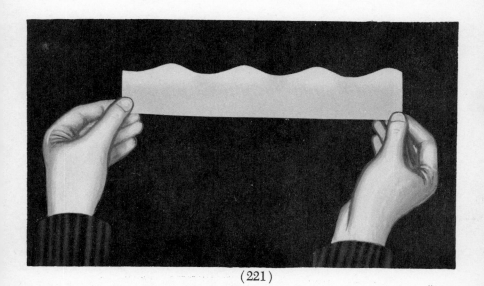

(221)

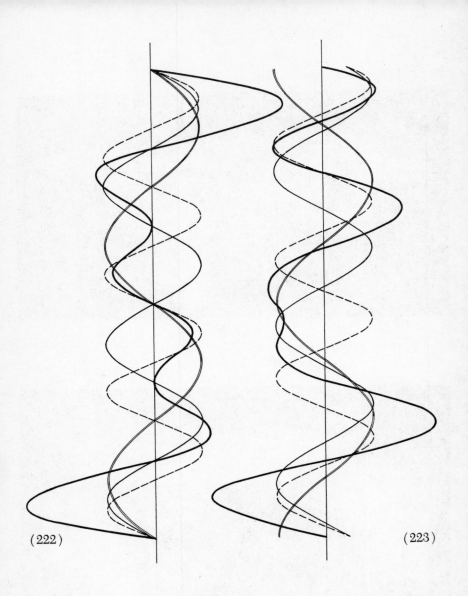

(222) (223)

of the component notes do not start simultaneously. As our ear perceives only the
intensity of the sound, which depends only
on the amplitude, and the pitch and 'color'
of the tune, which are determined by the

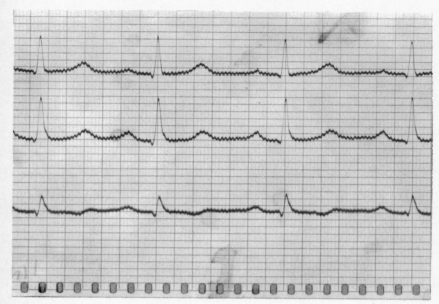

(224)

frequency of the vibrations, but is incapable of perceiving the crests and valleys of the acoustic waves, it hears the same continuous sound whenever the vibrations have started. In both cases the acoustic impression is identical whatever the geometrical difference between the recorded curves may be. There are not only two but an infinite number of different records, yielding the same acoustic impression, to be obtained from high $C:G:C$. This fact can be considered as a proof that our ear decomposes the sounds in sinusoidal components (harmonics) and, forming a compound again of them in the cerebro-nervous system, loses some characteristics of the true, physical process of sound. An electro-cardiogram (224) shows the electric vibrations in the nervous system, corresponding to the periodic play of the heart muscle. Its analysis is difficult.

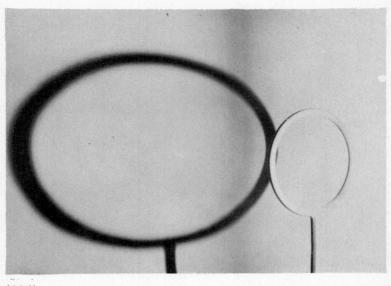

(225)

All the three familiar curves — ellipse, hyperbola, and parabola — can be got by cutting a cone with a plane in an appropriate manner. They can be obtained consequently as shadows of a circular disc. When we place the disc so that the whole shadow is on the wall, we get an ellipse (225); when a part of it casts no shadow on the wall, it is a hyperbola (226); when only a point is situated so as to give no shadow, it is a parabola (227). A ball lying on the table and illuminated from above casts an elliptic shadow and it touches the table at the focus of the ellipse.

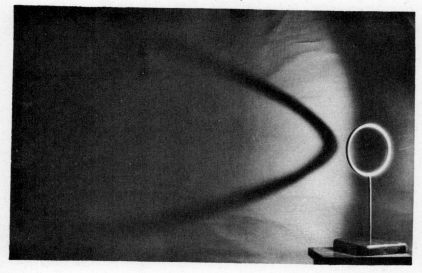

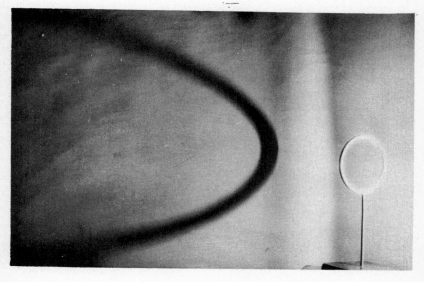

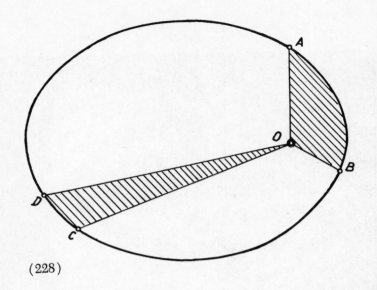

(228)

The planets wander on ellipses. The sun is one of the foci; the radius sun-planet covers the same area (228) every day (every hour, too) but the Earth does not cover the same distance every month, as the sketch indicates.

(229)

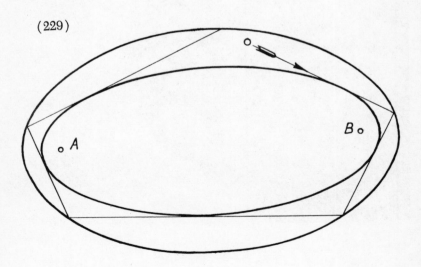

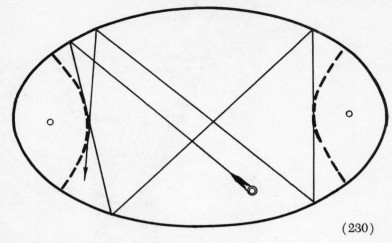

(230)

An elliptical billiard table (229) gives for a ball started so as not to pass between the foci a broken course and all the parts of it are tangents to a smaller ellipse with the same foci. If the initial stroke drives the ball between the foci (230), it will pass again between them after rebounding from the boundary. Thus it will forever do so; its path will consist of tangents to a hyperbola with the same foci as the table. If the ball starts at a focus, after hitting the boundary (231) it passes through the other focus; its course approaches the major axis very closely after a few rebounds.

(231)

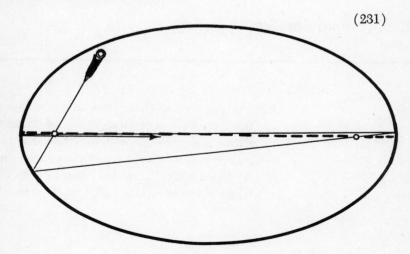

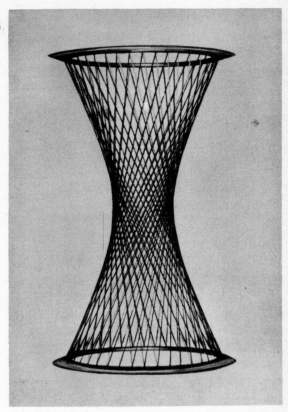

(232)

Surfaces Made of Straight Lines, the Chain, the Toycart, and the Minimal Surface

ALL the lines on the sphere are curved, but there are curved surfaces woven of straight lines. The cylinder and the cone, for instance, are such surfaces. We have seen the revolving cube (figure 148) gliding with its edges over two cones and a single-sheeted

hyperboloid of revolution. The general
single-sheeted hyperboloid is woven (232)
of two groups of straight lines, and, when
we look on it from above, we see (233) an
ellipse with its tangents. The paraboloid of
revolution arises when a parabola rotates
about its axis of symmetry. All the plane
sections of such a paraboloid, parallel to the
axis, give parabolas, and all these parabolas
are congruent. Thus the paraboloid of revolution is woven of an infinity of families of
congruent plane curves. The sphere and
the plane have the same property. (Are
there other examples?

A skew quadrilateral (234) whose vertices are loaded with equal weights has a
center of gravity that may be found by first
taking the center of gravity of one pair of
weights, then that of the other pair, and

(233)

(234)

then the center of these two centers (after having invested them with the united masses of the pairs they represent). This procedure gives the midpoint of the line connecting the midpoints of opposite sides. As it is possible to begin with the other pair of opposite sides, and as this will obviously lead us to the same center of gravity, it will be found that the lines connecting the midpoints of opposite sides of a skew quadrilateral intersect (and halve) each other. If the weights are unequal (e.g. a, b, c, d) but proportional ($a{:}b=c{:}d$), we get lines dividing one pair of opposite sides in the ratio $a{:}b$ and the other in the ratio $b{:}d$. These lines also intersect each other, as can be verified by the same argument. Now we can change the weights a, b, c, d but retain the proportionality; we obtain two groups of lines, which form a doubly woven surface (235) on the frame of the quadrilateral (the photograph shows a metal contour that is immaterial; we must choose four threads on

(235)

the model to have the skew quadrilateral).
Seen from the side, this surface looks (236)
like a saddle; it is called a hyperbolic paraboloid.

(236)

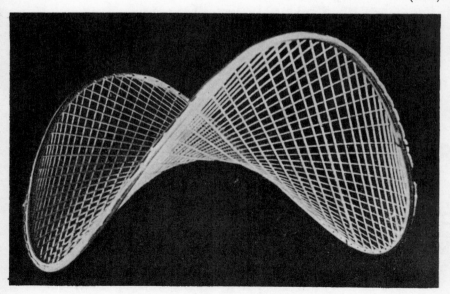

(237)

A simple method to get a surface with a family of straight lines on it is to take a plane wire with rods tangentially attached to it and twist it to make a skew curve. We obtain a double-sheeted surface (237) woven of a single group of straight lines;

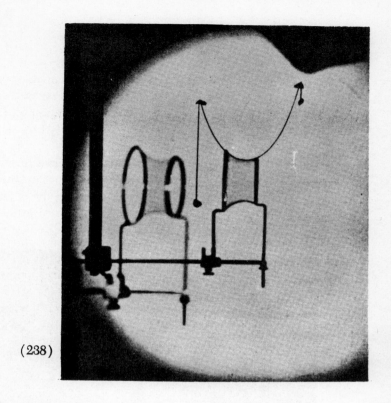

(238)

the curve is a sharp edge connecting the two sheets and no sheet extends beyond this edge. If we make two rings of wire upon the same axis (hence placed like the upper and lower bases of a truncated cone) and dip them into soap suds, there will arise a surface of revolution (238), the smallest of all those that may be stretched upon such a fixed frame, because a soap film makes itself as small as possible. The photograph shows both the actual surface itself and its shadow projected on a screen. Its parallels of latitude are circles; its meridian, which is distinctly visible as the upper contour of the shadow on the screen, can be enlarged by means of a projector. Then we can take its photograph together with a chain hanging on the screen, and we see that it is distinctly a catenary in form, that is, it has the appearance of a chain hanging between two nails (239). The equation of the catenary is $y=a(b^x+b^{-x})$; with appropriate units for x and y, it is $y=10^x+10^{-x}$.

To return to the minimal surface of soap suds, we have only to rotate the catenary round its x axis. Now, if the chain is given, we do not see any axis. To find it we have to cut the chain at its lowest point and

(239)

straighten it. Let us imagine the chain hanging on a wall and a set of nails on the concave side of the chain preventing it from going back; it would be sufficient then to let the chain fall by the action of gravity. The end of the chain would trace the same path as the toy cart (240) of a child walking along the pavement and dragging the cart in the street behind. The pavement will never be reached by the cart, which approaches it more and more; the pavement's edge is the axis sought for. Thus we find it as the highest of all horizontal lines that cannot be touched by the end of the chain cut at its lowest point and allowed to fall freely down.

The tractrix traced by the toy (or the developed chain) can be turned about the child's route as axis (i.e. about the same axis as that found for the catenoid) to give a new surface of revolution, which has the property that a lamina fitted to it may wander all over its surface, bending without stretching, always fitting the surface, and never crumpling. The same property is shared by the sphere, the cylinder, the cone, the plane, and by all surfaces got by folding the plane. Our surface has, however, the peculiarity of negative curvature; every point of it is a saddle point.

(240)

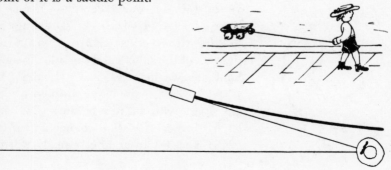

Platonic Bodies Again, Crossing Bridges, Tying Knots, Coloring Maps, and Combing Hair

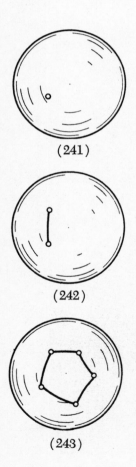

(241)

(242)

(243)

WE have stated previously that there are only five regular polyhedra, the so-called five Platonic bodies, without giving any reason why this is so. Let us draw on a sphere a figure having L lines, V vertices, and F faces; in other words, let us divide the globe into F countries (we shall consider seas and oceans as land). Then we shall have $V+F=L+2$, whatever the political situation may be. It is not difficult to verify this rule, discovered by Euler, the great Swiss mathematician. Let us start with one vertex (241); taking the rule to the letter, we see its truth in this case, because there is one vertex ($V=1$), one face ($F=1$), and no lines ($L=0$): $1+1=0+2$. Drawing one line from the vertex (242), we get a new division of the sphere and the rule obviously holds, as we have $V=2$, $F=1$, and $L=1$ ($2+1=1+2$). Now let us suppose we had any figure with the rule holding (243) and let us draw a new line connecting (244), (245) a vertex to another already existing vertex. We thus increase the number of vertices by 0, the number of faces by 1, and the number of lines by 1; this step means increasing by 1 the left and the right side of Euler's rule and it would obviously hold for the new division if it held before. If the new line ends with a new vertex (246), the increase in the number of vertices is 1, that of faces 0, and that of lines 1; the argument applies again. As we can draw any figure on the sphere, beginning with a vertex and then tracing the necessary lines one after another, Euler's rule is established. (What is the connection with dominoes?) Among all possible divisions of the sphere the regular ones in which we are interested are characterized by having the same number f of lines as a boundary of every face and the same number v of lines meeting at every vertex. If there are F faces, the product Ff gives the total number of lines, each line being counted twice, because each line belongs to two faces. Thus $2L=Ff$. We can also count the lines vertex by vertex; this gives $2L=Vv$. Thus we get

$$F=2L/f, \quad V=2L/v;$$

replacing V and F in Euler's rule by the fractions found here, we get

$$2L/v+2L/f=L+2,$$

which can be written also as

(E) $$1/v+1/f-1/2=1/L.$$

The easiest way to satisfy this equation is to put either

$$f=2, \quad v=L \quad \text{or} \quad v=2, \quad f=L.$$

The first assumption gives $F=L$, $V=2$. So we have only two vertices and as many faces as lines; as $v=L$, every line belongs to

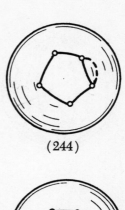

(244)

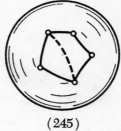

(245)

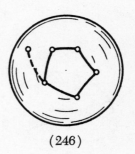

(246)

(247)

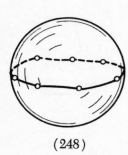

(248)

(249)

every vertex, and as $f=2$, every face is bounded by two lines. Thus we have two poles (247) joined by L meridians; the number of meridians is arbitrary ($L=1$, 2, 3, . . .). The second assumption gives $V=L$, $F=2$. Now we have only two faces and as many vertices as lines; as $f=L$, every line belongs to every face, i.e. the common boundary of the two faces is composed of L lines and L vertices. Thus we have the globe (248) divided in two hemispheres separated by an L-gon; the number L is arbitrary. We shall call these two kinds of maps exceptional; let us remark that the case $f=2$, $v=2$ belongs to both of them (249).

Returning to the general equation (E), let us try $L=1$; we can see easily that the only solutions we get are the exceptional ones, $v=1$, $f=2$ or $v=2$, $f=1$, already found. The same thing applies to $L=2$, which gives only the solution $f=v=2$ mentioned above. Thus to get new divisions of the sphere we must assume $L=3$, 4, 5. . . . The right side of (E) then becomes less than 1 and, as it is always greater than 1/2, we have

$$1/2 < 1/f + 1/v < 1$$

The value $f=1$ is incompatible with the right inequality and the value $f=2$ gives the exceptional cases of Figure 247, already dealt with. Let us begin then with $f=3$. We can try here only $v=3$, 4, and 5, because $v=1$ is incompatible with the right inequality, $v=2$ gives a case dealt with before, and $v=6$ or more gives for the sum $1/f+1/v=1/3+1/v$ the value 1/2 or less, contrary to the left inequality. The same argument shows that putting f greater than 3, we are limited to $v=3, 4, 5$, by the left inequality. As we can begin with v (which must be 3 at least, if we are to avoid impossible or exceptional cases), we see that f is limited to 3, 4, and 5. We have consequently $3 \times 3 = 9$ cases combining the two sets 3, 4, 5. Four of them,

$$f=4, v=4; \qquad f=4, v=5;$$
$$f=5, v=4; \qquad f=5, v=5;$$

are impossible because of the left inequality; $1/4+1/4=1/2$ is already too small. Five cases are left:

(a) $f=3, v=3$; (E) gives here
$$1/3+1/3-1/2=1/L, L=6, F=4, V=4$$

(b) $f=3, v=4$; (E) gives here
$$1/3+1/4-1/2=1/L, L=12, F=8, V=6$$

(c) $f=3, v=5$; (E) gives here
$$1/3+1/5-1/2=1/L, L=30, F=20, V=12$$

(d) $f=4, v=3$; (E) gives here
$$L=12, F=6, V=8$$

(e) $f=5, v=3$; (E) gives here
$$L=30, F=12, V=20.$$

We have simplified the computation by interchanging f with v and F with V to get immediately (d) from (b) and (e) from (c). We have finally found the five regular divisions of the sphere. The exceptional solutions yield no polyhedra in the usual sense, because we have neither two-sided polygons with straight sides nor two-faced polyhedra with plane faces. The five Platonic bodies corresponding to (a), (b), (c), (d), and (e) are the only regular polyhedra: tetrahedron, octahedron, icosahedron, cube, and dodecahedron.

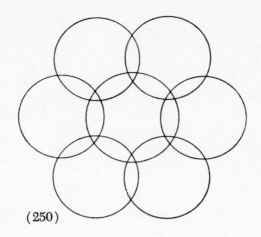

(250)

Let us realize that we have proved much more than we promised. We have found all regular maps on the globe whatever the frontiers may be, without any assumptions in regard to their being circles or tortuous lines. Moreover, the exact shape of the globe is immaterial for our statements, which hold as well for a cube- or a lens-shaped planet as for a spherical one.

(251)

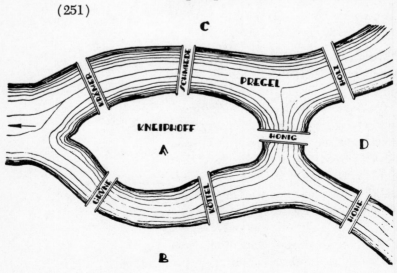

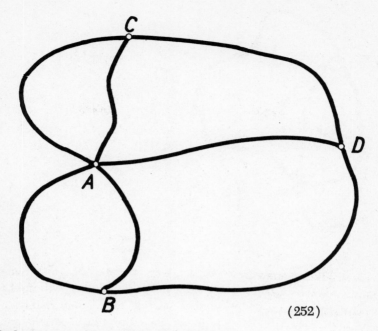

(252)

Such things are similar to the old problem
of drawing figures without lifting the pencil
and passing once and only once through
each point. The answer is affirmative for
this drawing (250). Euler came across the
question of what figures can be so drawn
when he was set the problem of the
Königsberg bridges (251). There are seven
of them, and the question is this: is it possible to cross them all in turn, passing no
more than once over each? If we indicate
the island by A, the left bank of the river by
B, the right one by C, and the area between
the two arms of the upper course by D, our
task will consist in drawing, with one stroke
of the pencil, a certain figure (252) con-
sisting of seven lines. The task is, however,
impossible, for having chosen any given
point as the point of departure and any
other as the goal, we should have to pass,

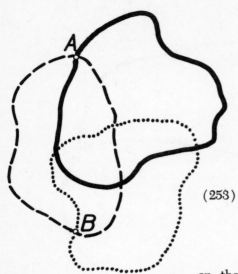

(253)

on the way, through at least two points A, B, C, D (i.e. through those that are neither starting nor ending points). Every time we pass through a certain point, we describe an entering and a departing path, i.e. two paths, and, as three or five lines meet at each point, certain lines remain undrawn. On the other hand, every figure with an even number of lines meeting at every point, or with two exceptional points where an odd number is allowed, can be drawn with one stroke, if its parts are connected. To prove it in the case of only even points, let us start at an arbitrary point. As there is at every point a departure if there is an entrance, the path must end at the starting point, whatever the tactics we have chosen. We can consider the whole path as a closed curve; if there remain parts of the figure not already visited, they must be linked with the paths in one of its points A; of the paths leading to A, an even number belong to the old path and an even number to the other parts.

Now let us travel round the closed curve beginning at A and finishing at A (253). As A belongs to the other part too, we can choose it now for a starting point and draw a new, closed curve from A to A. It is easy to see that two closed curves with a common point A can be considered as one closed curve (as the figure 8 is one). If our task is not yet accomplished, this new closed curve must be linked at B with the rest of the figure; this reasoning can be applied anew and leads finally to the solution. The case of two exceptional points of odd order is to be treated similarly. We have only to start at an exceptional point O; it is obvious that whatever way we choose, it will end at the other point of odd order O'. The rest of the figure has no exceptional points; it is therefore a closed curve linked at a certain point B (254) with the first path O-O'. Now we can start at O, go on the path O-O' to B, travel round the closed curve back to B, and finish the journey by B-O' on the first path.

(254)

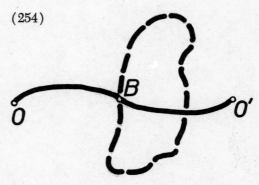

221

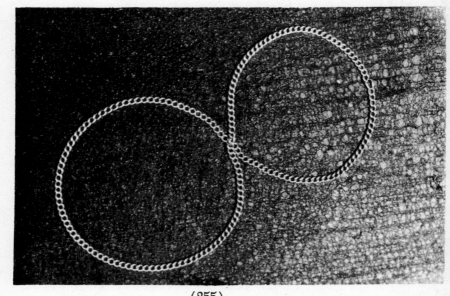

(255)

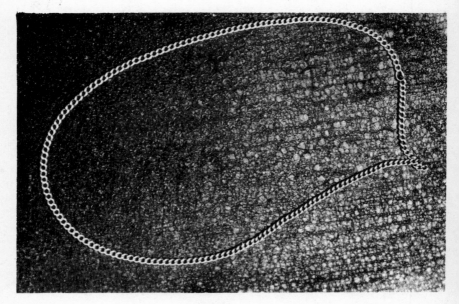

(256)

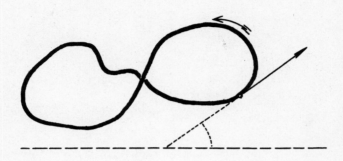

(257)

Let us look at a closed chain that (255) crosses itself once. When we move it on the table so as to let the crossing vanish, we must pass through a stage (256) when the chain 'breaks,' i.e. when a sharp point appears. To prove this statement, let us consider the tangent (257). Its angle with a fixed direction changes when we travel round the chain, but its increments are cancelled by its decrements, and the total variation during the whole circuit is zero. For a chain without crossing, the total variation is 360°; thus there must be a last shape of the chain with the variation zero; it is just the shape with a sharp point, where the tangent cancels abruptly at one point the variation of its angle acquired during the whole circuit.

(258)

The sketch (258) illustrates an allied problem. Here we have three houses, a dovecot, a well, and a haystack; three paths are to be traced from each house, one to the dovecot, one to the well, and the third to the haystack, but so arranged that they do not intersect each other. The problem proves to be impossible, for, if we connect the first house with the well, the haystack, and the dovecot, and then proceed through these points along the paths connecting them with the second house, we shall have three lines leading from one house to the other (259) and never crossing. These lines obviously

(259)

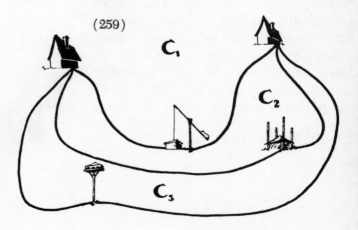

C_1

C_2

C_3

224

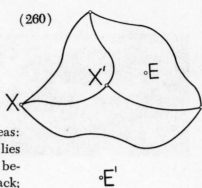

(260)

divide the whole plane into three areas: C_1, C_2, C_3. Now, the third house surely lies in one of them. If it lies in C_1, it will be beyond the closed line including the haystack; if in C_2, it will be within another closed line, while the dovecot will be outside; if in C_3, it will be embraced by a line beyond which the well lies. In the first case, the haystack will remain unconnected with the house, in the second, with the dovecot, in the third, with the well.

Let us consider four countries, every pair being neighbors. Their capitals can, therefore, be connected by railways, each line running only through the territories of the two terminal stations. Beginning with three capitals A, B, C, we get a sort of triangle. The capital D is interior or exterior to this triangle; joining it by railways to A, B, and C, we get, in both cases, a great triangle composed of three adjacent triangular parts. Now consider the capital E of a fifth country; it (260) must lie either in one of the small triangles or outside the great one. In either case there is one capital X (A, B, C, or D) separated from E by a triangle of railways. Since these lines pass entirely through territories belonging neither to X nor to E, the capital E is no neighbor of X. Thus five countries are never neighbors of each other.

(261)

Topology is the name for the chapter of geometry with which we are dealing here, and the science of knots also belongs to it. A cord with its ends connected (261) remains unknotted forever, if no knot has been tied on it before splicing; if, however, there initially was a knot (262), it never disappears (263) without cutting the string. The simplest knot can assume two distinct forms (264), which cannot be transformed into each other by pulling the string without cutting it; one is a mirror image of the other.

(262)

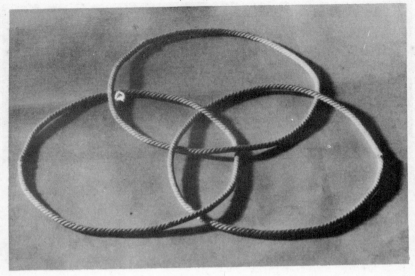

It is possible to shift a knot along a string as far as we like, but it is impossible to tie two knots on two ends of a string in such a manner that when brought together, they may cancel each other; no proof is known for this experimental fact.

It is easy to make three closed curves interlocked as a whole (265) with no pair of them being interlocked; it is to be seen at once that a cut in any of the strings lets all three fall asunder. It is even possible to make a model of any number of closed curves (266A, B) with the same properties.

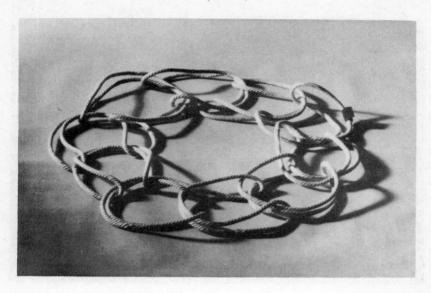

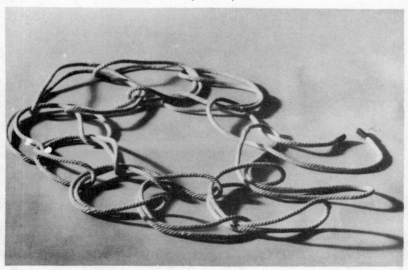

(267)

(268)

A strip of paper twisted through an angle of 180° and gummed together (the so-called Möbius band) is a unilateral surface (267). A fly may crawl over the whole of it without the inconvenience of crossing its edge. This

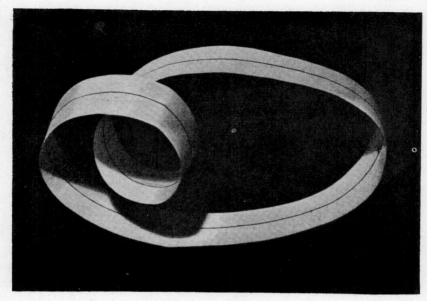

(269)

edge forms one closed, but not knotted, curved line. If we cut the Möbius band along the black line parallel to the edges, it does not fall asunder, but forms a bilateral (268) surface. The strip has now two closed curved lines as margins; they are not knotted, but interwoven. A simpler band having the same properties (bilateral surface, two interwoven, not knotted margins) may easily be obtained (269) by twisting a paper ribbon to an angle of 360° before gumming it, while the first band is twisted to 720°. There is another surface of exactly the same properties as the band of Figure 269: it is its image in the mirror; they cannot be transformed into each other by bending and twisting·without cutting. The surface, when cut along the middle line gives rise to two strips (270) interlocked with each other; both are of the same kind as the

(270)

original surface. If we twist the ribbon to the extent of three semirevolutions, that is, to 540°, before gumming, the result will again be a unilateral surface (271), the edge of which will be one knotted curve, the knot being of the kind seen on the left side of Figure 264. An ordinary sheet, a leaf for instance, is two-sided, its edge unknotted.

(271)

Hence arises the question: does there exist a bilateral surface with a knotted edge? A positive answer to this query is the model beneath (272). The edge is again a knot like the one on the left side of Figure 264.

(272)

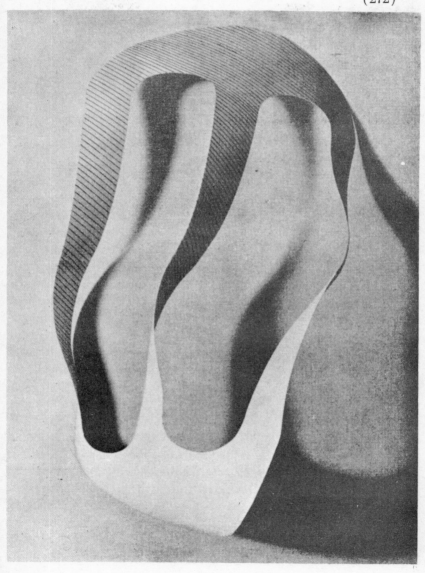

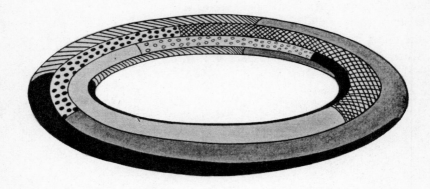

(273)

It is well-known that one may color any map in four hues, so that the neighboring countries are distinguishable from each other by their different colors. This fact has not been proved rigorously, but experiment has shown it to be so. For a torus (273), i.e. a surface in the form of a pneumatic tire, we should require as many as seven colors, for it is possible to draw a map on it showing seven countries, each of them contiguous with all others. The views of the torus from above and from beneath (274) give the disposition of the seven countries. On the other hand, it has been rigorously proved that seven colors are always sufficient for a map on a torus.

It is possible to draw on the torus a closed line that does not cross itself and is identical with the left-hand knot in Figure 264 (275A). By cutting the torus along the black line, i.e. along the knot, we get a bilateral surface (275B) with two edges; they are interlocked and both of them are knots of the same kind as the original one. To build

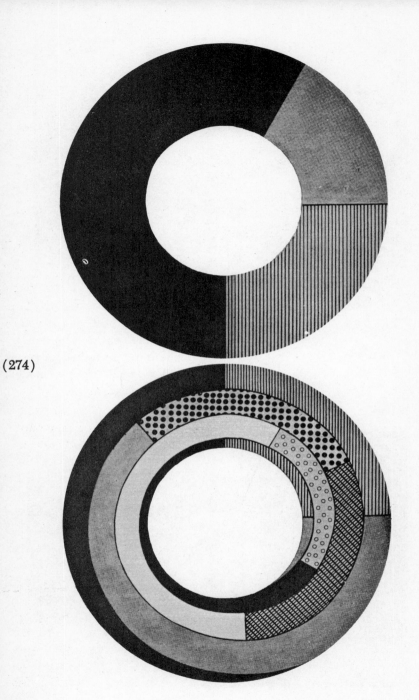

(274)

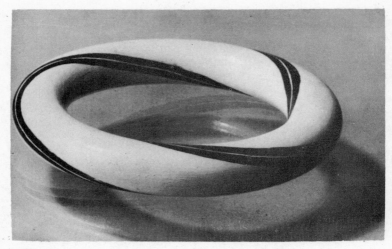

(275 A)

(275 B)

it up directly, we must twist a strip by three full revolutions (1080°) and knot it before gumming. A bilateral surface limited by two knotted but not interlocked edges is obtained by a junction (276) of two models of a previously described shape.

(276)

(277)

It is possible (277) to place on the torus any number of knots of the left-hand type in Figure 264 with no one of them cutting itself or any other. If, however, we place both knots of Figure 264 on a torus, they will produce 12 intersections (278).

(278)

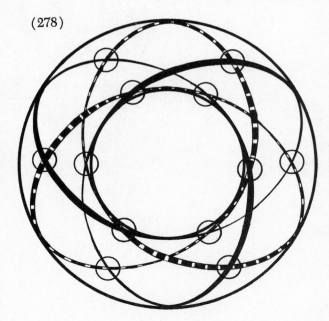

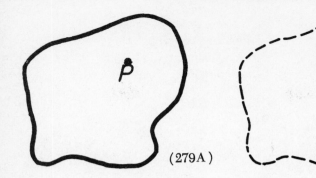

(279A)

(279B)

If a flat region of any kind (279 A, B) made of an elastic material contracts so as to occupy finally only a part of the area it originally covered, there will be always a point (P) that occupies the same place after contraction as before. The proof is not difficult if we admit the property of chessboards mentioned in the section on chess puzzles. If a sphere made of an elastic tissue is folded and distorted (but not torn) so as to become flat, there are necessarily two antipodes, A and B, which come to lie one upon another in the new situation (280 A, B). There is a curious consequence of this theorem: at every time there is on our globe a pair of antipodes having both the same temperature and the same air pressure. A hairy sphere cannot be combed

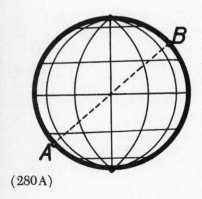

(280A)

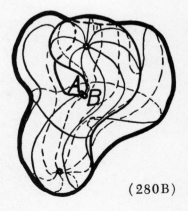

(280B)

smoothly as a whole; there is always at least one whirlpoint (281 A, B) where the hair has no definite direction.

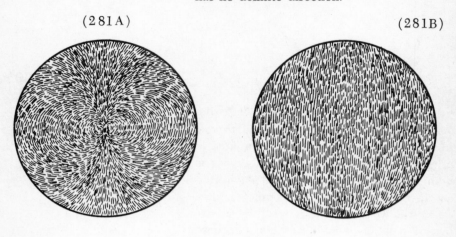

Board of Fortune, Frogs, Freshmen, and Sunflowers

THE laws of nature lead to various curves. On the diagram (282) the full lines show the connection between the pressure P and the volume V of one kilogram of gas. The full lines are isotherms, i.e. lines of the same temperature. According to the law of Boyle and Mariotte, they are hyperbolas. Hydrogen (H_2) is represented by two isotherms, one for 0°, the other for 77°. The law of Boyle and Mariotte is $PV=$ constant. The dotted lines appear when at a certain moment (the point indicated on the diagram by a small circle) the vessel is surrounded

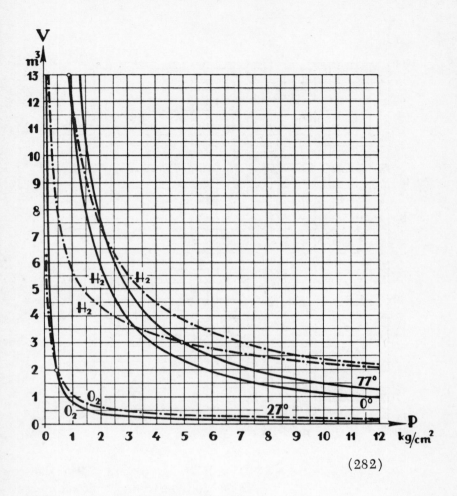

(282)

by a coating impervious to heat. The temperature then changes in accordance with the decrease or increase of pressure and we obtain adiabatic lines: they are generalized hyperbolas ($P^a.V^b =$ constant). If we plot P and V on logarithmic scales (cf. Figure 71), all the lines (283) become straight.

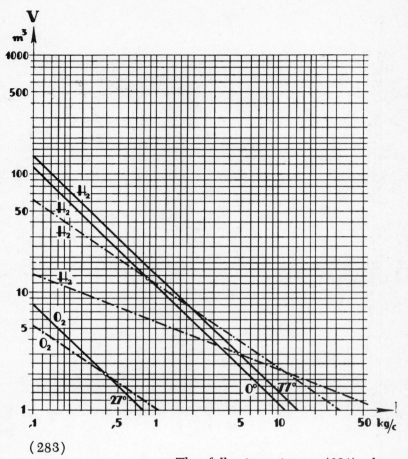

(283)

The following picture (284) shows a system of eyelets with channels leading between them. We can imagine it to be a plan of a town. People coming in hesitate at every bifurcation, trying to decide whether they are to choose the left or the right street. There is first only one street downtown and therefore no choice. As to the two following streets in the direction NS, one gets into the left one by avoiding the first eyelet to the left; by avoiding it to the right, he gets into the right street. These possibilities can be noted as 1, 1. Next we

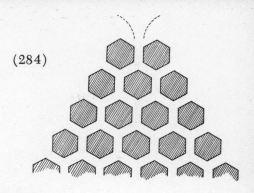

have three streets *NS*. Only the man who
has already chosen 'left' can get into the
western one. This possibility may be
noted by 1. To get into the middle one,
there are two possibilities: one can cancel
the first choice 'left' by choosing now
'right,' or the man who first chose 'right'
may now choose 'left.' As to the eastern
street, there is only one possible way to get
there. These possibilities may be noted as
1, 2, 1. By adding the neighboring numbers, we get from 1, 2, 1 the set 1, 3, 3, 1,
which obviously represents all possibilities
for the next four streets. By proceeding in
this manner, we obtain Pascal's triangle.

$$1$$
$$1 \quad 1$$
$$1 \quad 2 \quad 1$$
$$1 \quad 3 \quad 3 \quad 1$$
$$1 \quad 4 \quad 6 \quad 4 \quad 1$$
$$1 \quad 5 \quad 10 \quad 10 \quad 5 \quad 1$$
$$1 \quad 6 \quad 15 \quad 20 \quad 15 \quad 6 \quad 1$$
$$1 \quad 7 \quad 21 \quad 35 \quad 35 \quad 21 \quad 7 \quad 1$$
$$1 \quad 8 \quad 28 \quad 56 \quad 70 \quad 56 \quad 28 \quad 8 \quad 1$$
$$1 \quad 9 \quad 36 \quad 84 \quad 126 \quad 126 \quad 84 \quad 36 \quad 9 \quad 1$$

The last line on the diagram represents in how many ways the people can reach the first, the second . . . the tenth street of the tenth row. The total number of possibilities for this row is $1+9+36+84+126+126+84+36+9+1=512=2^9$. In anthropology, the human stature, for instance, may be considered a result of many causes acting in the course of its development, some of which tend to lower the stature, others to increase it. We can imagine every individual choosing by tossing a coin whether he takes from nature an inch more to his stature or gives away from what he has got already. If he is allowed to do it nine times and if there are 512 people doing the same, we can guess by analogy with the people walking through the town what will probably happen. We can consider each loss of an inch as a decision to go right, each gain as a decision to go left. As there are 512 people, we can exhaust all possibilities written in the last line of Pascal's triangle. If they all occur, we shall have 1 man five inches short of the average stature, 9 men four inches shorter than the average, 36 men three inches shorter . . . 126 men one inch shorter than the average, 126 men one inch over the average, 84 men two inches over the average . . . 1 man five inches over the average stature. If we place them so that the tallest stand in the foremost rank, those shorter by an inch in the second rank, and so on, we shall have ten ranks, and the right wing of the squad will form a curve determined by Pascal's numbers, provided that the left one has been arranged as a straight line. We can get this curve of Gauss in several ways. First we can draw it

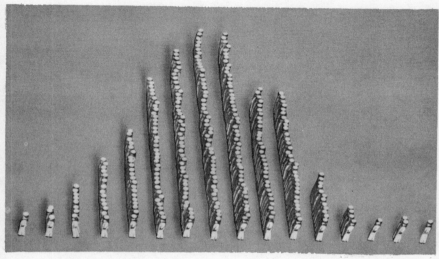

(285)

taking Pascal's numbers as ordinates. Then we can assemble, for instance, all Princeton freshmen of a year and place them in ranks according to their stature (285). Finally, we can make a wooden 'board of fortune' (286) with hexagonal eyelets and channels between them, as already described. By inclining the board and pouring small beads into the funnel at the top, we could catch them in boxes beneath the last row of channels and verify the Gauss law of chance by determining whether the columns of beads in actual tests are more or less proportionate to Pascal's numbers. We can simplify the last experiment by employing

(286)

a board without eyelets (287, 288); we only pour beads from one point and catch them in boxes. This procedure corresponds to an infinity of infinitely small eyelets; the

(287)

exact Gauss law, of which Pascal's triangle
gives only an approximation, has been established mathematically only for an infinity of infinitely small causes working

(288)

independently. The boxes on the lower
edge are necessary in order to prevent later
incoming beads from changing the position
of the former by pressure.

Trevan's experiments on the action of digitalis on the frog showed that of a hundred frogs subjected to the injections of digitalis, indicated on the horizontal (logarithmic) scale (dose for each 10 decagrams of the frog's weight), as many die as are to be found on the sketch to the left of the vertical line (289) defined by that dose. An injection of 0.4 cc (per 100 g), for instance, will suffice in 6 cases, while one of 0.6 cc, will kill in 50 cases. (How much is necessary to kill 100 frogs?) Of course, these are average figures of many tests. The curve of the 'frog line' is, in this case also, Gauss's curve; its equation is

$$y = A . 10^{c(x-b)^2} \quad (c \text{ is negative}).$$

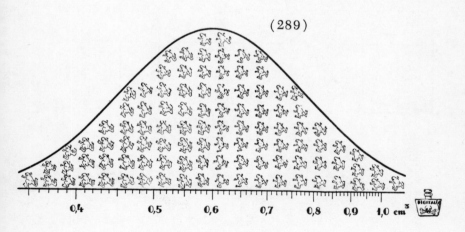

(289)

In matters connected with the development of organisms within a limited space, we find another type of curve. Thornton discovered that bacteria kept in a closed vessel develop with regard to the volume they

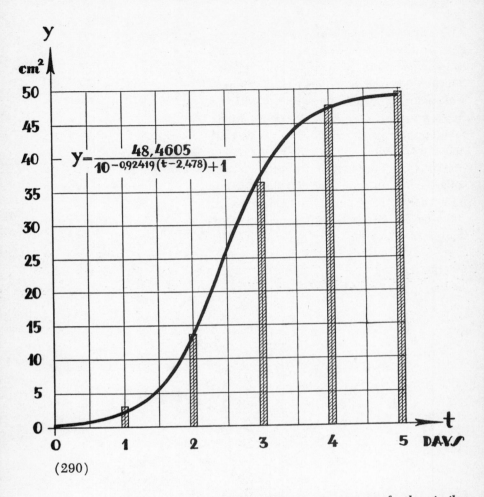

$$y = \frac{48,4605}{10^{-0,92419(t-2,478)}+1}$$

(290)

occupy — in a manner perfectly similar (290) to that of sunflowers (as shown by experiments of Reed and Holland) (291) with regard to the average height, or to that of the American railways with regard to the total length (292). The reason for this development is that the increase is proportional to the number of organisms already living, as well as to the (decreasing) space still available. The drawings show also the small discrepancies between the theoretic

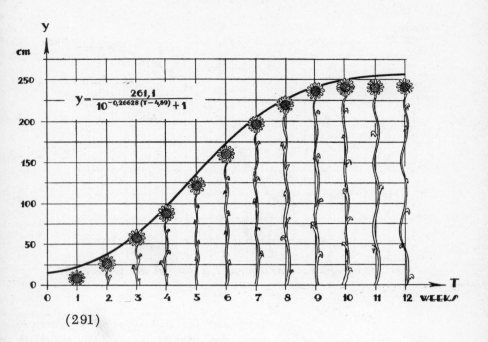

$$y = \frac{261,1}{10^{-0,26628\,(T-4,89)}+1}$$

(291)

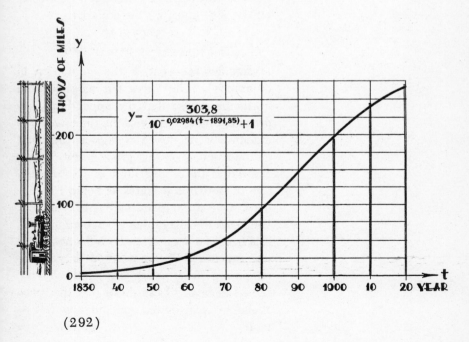

$$y = \frac{303,8}{10^{-0,02984\,(t-1891,85)}+1}$$

(292)

251

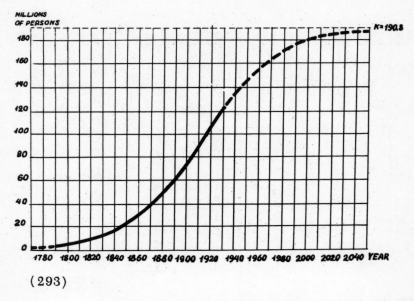

(293)

curve and the real data. The American population exhibits the same law of growth (293); it is given by the equation

$$Y = \frac{190830.35}{1 + 10^{1.542035 - 0.01366265 \ (t - 1800)}}$$

(t signifies the year, Y the population in thousands). The curve has an inflection; it can be shown that the upper limit, approached by the curve as the time increases indefinitely, lies twice as high as the point of inflection. On this ground statisticians calculated the upper limit of the population of the United States as being 160 millions. Our curve gives around 191 millions. Whatever one may think of such arguments, it is true that soon after the inflection point was reached, bills were voted to stop immigration; other symptoms could be observed in favor of the thesis that the space available was limited and already felt as such.

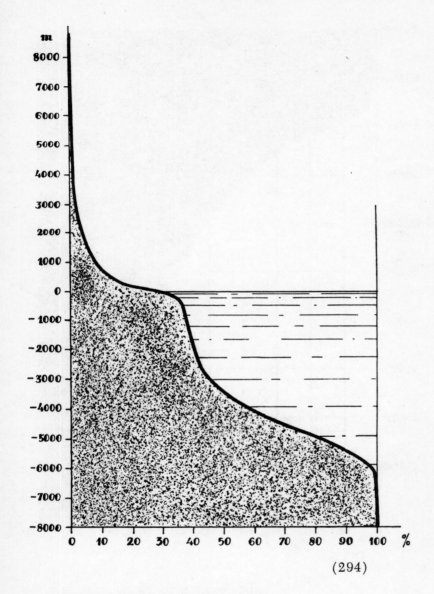

(294)

We have also a great many other curves
in the domain of natural science, though
their laws are not based upon theoretical
deduction: e.g. the curve showing the distribution (294) of land and sea at various

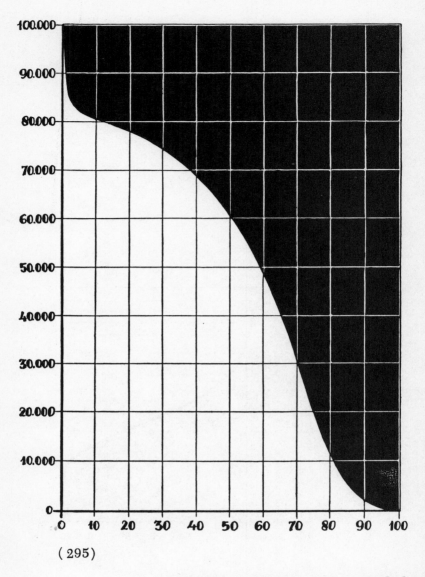

(295)

altitudes (in percentages) or a graph showing the mortality of males in the United
States (295).

Notes

(The numbers refer to the illustrations or to the relevant text.)

(1) H. E. Dudeney, *Amusements in Mathematics,*
London, 1917, p. 27.

(2) Pythagoras of Samos (c. 582-507 B.C.), the
author of the theorem on right triangles, considered the problem of regular tessellations and
the theory of musical harmony. The dissection,
however, is a Hindu achievement; the original drawing bears the inscription 'Look!' which must con-
vince the reader better than any verbal argument.

(4) F. Morley, 'On reflexive geometry,' *Trans.
Amer. Math. Soc.* 8 (1907), pp. 14-24; J. M. Child,
'Proof of Morley's Theorem,' *Math. Gazette,* 11
(1923), p. 171.

(5) T. Ważewski, in *Ann. de la Soc. Polonaise de
Mathématique,* 18 (1945) p. 164, quotes a lawyer,
Mr. Rappaport, as the author of this trisection. The
error is less than 22′ 23″; for angles less than 30°
it is less than 1′.

(6) We have not considered the question of *all* the
squares' being of different sizes; to make it still
more difficult we could prescribe a limit not to be
surpassed by the size of the squares employed.

(7) This decomposition of the rectangle was given
by Z. Moroń, in Przegląd *Mat.-Fiz.* 3 (1925), pp.
152-3.

(8) R. L. Brooks, C. A. B. Smith, A. H. Stone, and
W. T. Tutte, in *Duke Math. Journal,* 7 (1940), pp.
312-40; the dissection is given on p. 333. The au-
thors establish a connection between the problem
of dissection and properties of electric currents in
networks. The impossibility of decomposing a rectangle into less than 9 squares has been proved by
H. Reichardt and H. Toepken, in *Jahresbericht d.
Deutschen Math. Vereinigung,* 50 (1940), 'Auf-
gaben u. Lösungen,' pp. 13-14.

(9) H. E. Dudeney, op. cit., p. 27. J. G.-Mikusiński, *Ann. Univ. M. Curie-Skłodowska*, 1 (1946), (Section A), pp. 45-50, gives the graphical demonstration (p. 49).

(11) W. Ahrens gives the theory of different games in *Mathematische Unterhaltungen und Spiele*, Leipsic, Teubner, 1910; I, pp. 172-6. *The Theory of Games and Economic Behavior* is the title of a book by J. V. Neumann and O. Morgenstern (2nd edition, Princeton, 1947) in which the theory of games is subjected to a thorough logical and mathematical analysis.

(12) Dr. J. Berger, *Columbia Chess Chronicle*, 1888. According to the analysis of W. Hetper, the longest defense of Black is the following one:

White	Black	White	Black
1. *Q–QKt8*	*B–QB5*	8. *K–Kt3*	*B–KB6*
2. *Q–K5*	*B–QR3*	9. *Q–QB1*	*B–KR4*
3. *Q–K1*	*B–QKt4*	10. *Q–QR1*	*B–KKt4*
4. *Q–QB1*	*B–KB8*	11. *Q–KR8†*	*B–KR6*
5. *Q–KB4*	*B–QR3*	12. *Q×B†*	*B–KR7†*
6. *Q–KKt4*	*B–QKt2*	13. *Q×B††*	
7. *Q–Q1*	*B–K5*		

(13) W. Massmann, *Neue Leipziger Zeitung*, 1936. This problem is to be found in a book by F. J. Prokop, 1000 *auserlesene Schachaufgaben*, Prague, 1944, no. 423.

(14) Dr. K. Ebersz, *Magyar Sakkvilag*, 1940. The analysis was given by Duchamp and Halberstadt in *L'Opposition et les cases conjuguées*, Paris and Brussels, Lancel & Legrand, 1930, p. 111, No. 244. Torres y Quevedo constructed an automaton that, by means of the king and the rook, gives mate to the king, moved by a living partner, from an arbitrary initial position in the minimum number of moves; *Scientific American Supplement* 6 (1915), p. 296. The invention of electronic devices, such as those utilized in modern computing machines, makes it possible to imagine automata performing even more complicated tasks. (See *Cybernetics* by N. Wiener, Wiley, New York, 1948.)

(15, 16) Ref. 11, II, pp. 226-60. This game is said to have been invented by the famous chess player, S. Lloyd. The theory of the game was given by W. Johnson and W. E. Story in *American Journal of Mathematics* 2 (1879), pp. 397-404.

(18) Euclid, one of the greatest mathematicians of all time, lived in Alexandria about 300 B.C. He created the first systematic exposition of geometry. D. H. Lehmer devised a machine on a photoelectric basis that examines the divisibility of giant numbers; it was exhibited in 1933 at the Century of Progress Exhibition in Chicago. Since that time great progress in computing machines has been achieved by electronic devices. Cf. article by J. E. Littlewood about large numbers, in *Math. Gazette,* 32 (1948), pp. 163-171.

(20, 21) W. W. Rouse Ball, *Mathematical Recreations and Essays,* London, Macmillan & Co., 1939, pp. 165 and 171. Also Ahrens, op. cit., pp. 225 and 293.
(22) Dudeney, op. cit., pp. 102-3; Ahrens, op. cit., p. 381. The knight's tour was composed by a Russian officer, Jaenisch; *Chess Monthly,* 1859.

(23) Leonhard Euler (1707-83) of Basle was the author of several hundred papers touching almost all domains of higher and of elementary mathematics. The impossibility of arranging 36 officers was proved by Fisher and Yates, *Proc. Camb. Phil. Soc.* 30 (1944), pp. 492-507. See also Bruck and Ryser, *Canadian Journal of Math.* 1 (1949), pp. 88-93.

(24) R. A. Fisher, *The Design of Experiments,* Edinburgh, 1947.

(25-27) Socrates' pupil, Plato (429-348 B.C.), discusses the irrationality of $\sqrt{2}$ and of other numbers. The reader may consult the book by Richard Courant and Herbert Robbins, *What is Mathematics?* Oxford University Press, 1946, ch. 2, § 2.

(28-29) Blaise Pascal (1623-62), geometer and philosopher, discoverer of the barometer, the calculating machine, and the calculus of probabilities, applied mathematical induction in his *Traité du triangle arithmétique* in 1665. F. Maurolico (1494-1575) was his predecessor in this method (1575) but his work has been forgotten.

(30, 31) Lord Rayleigh, *The Theory of Sound*, London, 1894-6. L. Euler (see *n.* 23) treated the problem of the musical scale and called attention to the fact that the smaller are the numbers that show the ratio of vibrations, the better are the concords. Claudius Ptolemy (Alexandria, 140 B.C.) assumed as the starting point, besides the eighth, the fifth, and fourth, also the major third 5:4, and constructed a diatonic scale of intervals: 9/8, 10/9, 16/15, 9/8, 10/9, 9/8, 16/15. Here all the concords, together with the minor third, are expressed by numbers below ten, but the seconds vary: once 9/8, the other time 10/9. On a piano so tuned, a melody in C-major would sound otherwise than in D-major. The tempered scale was introduced by the organist Andreas Werckmeister in 1691.

(32) A. Zeising (1854) in his book *Neue Lehre von den Proportionen des menschlichen Körpers* attributes an exaggerated significance to the golden section.

(33) L. Fibonacci lived in Pisa about 1200. The idea visualized by the tree has been suggested by an article of E. Żyliński in the reports of the *International Mathematical Congress* in Bologna 4 (1928), pp. 153-6. (See also *Acta Soc. Botanicorum Poloniae* 5 (1928), pp. 380-91, in which the so-called Ludwig's Law or the role of Fibonacci's numbers in botany is discussed by D. Szymkiewicz.

(34) Palazzo della Cancellaria in Rome.

(36, 37, 38, 39) In (36) the area surveyed by C is one eighth of the whole pasture; in (37) it is already ¼; the point at which the three areas meet has ½, ⅝ as co-ordinates if $(0,0)$ and $(1,1)$ are the opposite corners of the pasture; in (38) the common point is 1/2, 13/24; in (39) the longest ride of A is $\sqrt{505}/48$, of C $\sqrt{601}/48$, the common point being the same as in (38).

(41, 42) J. Schreier, *Mathesis Polska*, 7 (1932), pp. 154-60.

(43, 44) $[x]$ means here the greatest integer not surpassing x. Thus [5.7], for instance, means 5, [6] means 6.

(46) C. A. B Smith, 'The counterfeit coin problem,' *The Mathematical Gazette*, 31 (1947), no. 293, pp. 31-9.

(47) M. C. K. Tweedie, in *The Mathematical Gazette*, 23 (1939), pp. 278-82, has given a graphical solution of the wine problem; our picture is a modification of his idea.

(48) This has been noticed by H. Auerbach and S. Mazur.

(49, 51) B. Knaster and H. Steinhaus, *Ann. de la Soc. Polonaise de Mathématiques*, 19 (1946), pp. 228-31. H. Steinhaus, *Econometrica*, 16 (1948), pp. 101-4.

(52) G. Pólya, *L'Enseignement Mathématique*, 4 (1919), pp. 355-79. The property of an equilateral triangle to make the sum of distances from its sides a constant is a theorem of Viviani.

(53, 54 . . . . . . 69). See *n.* 2.

(70-71) This question belongs to the same chapter as 241. It was proposed by the author to his students and answered by K. Florek and others.

(71, 72) The principle of a slide rule was given by E. Gunter in 1623. In 1671 S. Partridge designed an instrument similar to our present slide rule. If the product appears beyond the scales, we must place the number 10 (instead of 1) opposite the multiplier.

(74, 75) The law of the lens was discovered in 1693 by Edmond Halley, the famous English astronomer (1656-1724).

(76) The Minorite Marin Mersenne (1588-1648) arrived at the formula showing the number of vibrations of a string tensely stretched by way of experiment. The formula is valid for the units centimeter-gram-second; if the power P is given in weight units, it must be multiplied by 981 cm/sec^2 before being put into the formula.

(77) G. Pick, *Geometrisches zur Zahlenlehre,* *Ztschr. d. Vereines* 'Lotos,' Prague, 1899; H. Steinhaus, 'O polu figur płaskich,' *Przegląd Mat.-Fiz.,* 1924.

(78, 79, 80) H. F. Blichfeldt, *Transactions of the American Mathematical Society,* 15 (1914), pp. 227, 235.

(81) H. Minkowski, *Geometrie der Zahlen,* Leipsic, Teubner, 1912. Simplified proof: Hilbert and Cohn-Vossen, *Anschauliche Geometrie,* Berlin, Springer, 1932. The latter book contains many beautiful diagrams and photographs.

(82) G. Pólya.

(84, 85, 86, 87, 88) W. Sierpiński, *Bulletin de l'Academie des Sciences de Cracovie,* A, (1912), pp. 463-78. Such curves were first determined by G. Peano, an Italian mathematician.

(90) Schnirelmann.

(91, 92) H. Steinhaus, *Mitteilungen der Sächsischen Akad.* 82 (1930), pp. 120-30. *Przegląd Geogr.* 21 (1947) brings a notice by the same author where the average declivity of a district is defined by $\tan g = h \Sigma L_i / B$; B is the area of the district, h the vertical distance of two consecutive levels, L_i the length of the i-th level. Cf. an article by the same author in the *Comptes Rendus de la Soc. des Sciences et des Lettres de Wrocław,* série B, 1949, where the length of order n is defined in order to be applied to geographical questions.

(97, 98) The Italian geometer L. Cremona and the English physicist James C. Maxwell devised, about 1875, the 'graphical statics' based on the principle of reciprocal figures. It is used for calculating iron constructions.

(99) Apollonius of Perga (A.D. 100-170) studied the properties of conic sections.

(101) M. Warmus, *Ann. de la Soc. Polonaise de Mathématique,* 19 (1946), pp. 233-4, without proof.

(102, 103) A. Zięba gave this solution without proof.

(105) René Descartes, the creator of analytic geometry, mentions this spiral in a letter to Mersenne in 1638. The logarithmic spiral appears in nature when an organism grows in such a manner that it keeps its similitude to the shape it had in any previous stage. Cf. D'Arcy W. Thompson, *Science and the Classics,* Oxford University Press, 1940, pp. 114-47.

(106) The equation of this spiral is $r = ae^{c\varphi}$ ($e = 2.71828\ldots$, $c = 0.274411\ldots$, a arbitrary) r being the distance from the vertex and φ the angle against a fixed direction. The ship's course makes an angle of $74° 39' 12''$ with the line from vortex to ship.

(108) Archimedes (287-212 B.C.), one of the greatest mathematicians of all time, calculated the ratio of the circumference of a circle to its diameter correct to the third decimal point; he discovered the laws of floating bodies and the beginnings of higher mathematics. Cf. W. W. Rouse Ball, *A Primer of the History of Mathematics,* 4th edition, Macmillan & Co., London, 1895.

(109) Henry T. Brown, 507 *Mouvements mécaniques,* Liège, Desoer, p. 28, nos. 96, 97.

(110) Peaucellier, a French naval officer, discovered this linkage in 1864. He was anticipated by Sarrut (*Comptes de l'Académie de Paris,* 36 [1853], p. 1036), who approached the problem from a different side.

(113) L. Mascheroni, *Geometria del compasso,* Pavia, 1797. Napoleon I studied this book. Georg Mohr (*Euclides Danicus,* Amsterdam, 1672), who anticipated Mascheroni in constructions with the compass alone, has been forgotten. Cf. Book 27, ch. III, p. 5.

(114A) H. Rademacher and O. Toeplitz, *Zahlen und Figuren,* Berlin, Springer, 1930, p. 164.

(114B) Adam Kochański, a Polish Jesuit, published this construction in *Acta Eruditorum* in 1685. He was the first to apply a steel spring for suspension of the pendulum of a clock.

(116) Cf. A. H. Stone and J. W. Tukey on generalized 'sandwich' theorems in *Duke Math. Journal,* 9 (1942), pp. 356-9, and H. Steinhaus, *Fundamenta Mathematicae,* 33 (1945), pp. 245-63.

(118A) Nicholas Copernicus (1473-1543), the great astronomer, proved that the planets are circling around the sun and that the earth obeys this law too. His work, *De revolutionibus orbium coelestium,* appeared in 1543.

(119-122) John Bernoulli, one of the creators of higher mathematics, born in 1667, presented in 1696 the problem of the brachistochrone or the line of quickest fall, and solved it in the year following. The angular velocity ω of the wheel, its radius r, and the acceleration g of gravity are connected by $g = r\omega^2$.

(123) Immanuel Kant, the great German philosopher (1724-1804).

(124, 125) Cf. Book 27, ch. VII, § 8.

(126, 127) Cf. Book 114A.

(128) A problem proposed to college students in Russia. *Uspiechy Mat. Nauk,* 3 (1948), no. 2 (24), p. 239.

(129) K. Zindler ('Ueber konvexe Gebilde, II,' in *Monatshefte f. Math. u. Phys.* 31 [1921], pp. 25-9) noticed that there were curves, other than circles, whose chords halving the circumference also halve the area. H. Auerbach, 'Sur un problème de M. Ulam concernant l'équilibre des corps flottants,' in *Studia Mathematica* 7 (1938), pp. 121-2.

(130, 131) Cf. *nn.* 28, 29. Nicomedes lived about 200 B.C.

(133) Cf. Book 114A.

(134) The picture of Bernardino Pinturicchio (1454-1513) representing *The Return of Ulysses* (National Gallery, London).

(137) H. Steinhaus, 'Sur la localisation au moyen des rayons X,' *Comptes Rendus de l'Académie des Sciences,* Mai 1938. U. S. Patent Office nos. 2,441,-538, 11 May 1948: Method of and apparatus for localizing foreign bodies.

(139, 140, 141, 142) Invented by J. G.-Mikusiński.

(145, 146) K. W. Pohlke discovered this theorem in 1858 and published it in 1860 without giving the proof. The elementary proof was given by H. A. Schwarz in the *Journal f. Reine u. angewandte Mathematik* 63 (1864), pp. 309-14.

(147, 148) If we turn such a model quickly, we see black lines of an unexpected course. These are the points of apparent intersections of the edges moving along.

(157, 158) M. Brückner, *Vielecke and Vielflache,* Leipsic, 1900, p. 130. The cosine of the acute angle of the rhombus is 1/3.

(166-185) Cf. *nn.* 25-27. The volumes of the five regular solids of the edge *a* are
$a^3\sqrt{2}$ /12, a^3, $a^3\sqrt{2}$/3, $a^3(15 + 7\sqrt{5}$)/4, $5a^3(3 + \sqrt{5})$/12. See H. S. M. Coxeter, *Regular Polytopes,* New York, 1949, p. 22.

(193A) The faces of this dodecahedron cannot be *regular* pentagons, because of the crystallographic restriction. See Coxeter, op. cit., p. 63.

(196) Ibid., p. 69.

(200) Ibid., p. 96.

(202) The picture of the moon (inverted in the telescope) was taken by the Paris Observatory on 26 April 1898 at 7:09 P.M.

(203) A remark by M. Warmus.

(205) G. Mercator (1512-94). There are no projections preserving lengths unaltered.

(218-221) The equation of this curve is $y = a \sin bx$. The function 'sine' was introduced in the second century after Christ by the Alexandrian astronomer, Ptolemy.

(225, 226, 227) Cf. *n.* 99.

(228) The laws of the revolution of planets were discovered in 1609 by J. Kepler (1571-1630).

(235, 236) If $(a{:}b)/(c{:}d)$ has a constant value other than 1, then we shall obtain a hyperbolic paraboloid other than that given by the construction described in the text.

(238) This minimal surface is called a catenoid. Any given contour immersed in soap solution will give us a minimal surface bounded by the contour. (C. V. Boys, 'Soap Bubbles,' *Romance and Science Series,* London, 1924-5; there we also find a recipe for soap suds.)

(240, 241) F. Minding (1806-85) discovered this surface, and F. Beltrami (1835-1900) found that creatures living on such a surface would consider the non-Euclidean geometry of Lobatchevsky, with the sum of angles in a triangle smaller than 180°, as natural. N. Lobatchevsky (1793-1856) and J. Bolyai (1802-60) discovered that there are consistent geometries different from the Euclidean system. (Cf. Book 27, ch. IV, § 9.)

(241-249) Coxeter, op. cit., pp. 5-12.

(251) Cf. *n.* 22.

(259, 260) J. B. Listing (1808-82) published in 1847 the first book on topology. Cf. Book 27, ch. v.

(263) The problem of cancelling of knots was communicated to the author by K. Borsuk.

(267) A. F. Moebius (1790-1863). The band appears in his *Werke,* vol. 2 (1858), p. 519.

(272, 273) The four-color problem was proposed by Moebius in 1840. It has been proved for all maps containing less than 38 regions by Philip Franklin, *Journal of Mathematics and Physics,* 16 (1937), pp. 172-84. A simple proof of Heawood's theorem that five colors are sufficient for every map is to be found in Book 27, Appendix to ch. v. For an account of the seven-color theorem see Book 20, p. 235.

(279) Proposed by H. Lebesgue in *Mathematische Annalen*, 70 (1911), pp. 166ff.; the proof is not sufficient; proved by L. E. J. Brouwer in *Journal f. reine u. angewandte Mathematik*, 142 (1913), pp. 150ff. The proof based on the property of chessboards employs an idea of W. Stożek. We consider the chessboard as the region and Q as the position of point P after contraction. We call a square white if PQ has its horizontal component directed to the right for every point P belonging to the square, black if the foregoing holds with 'right' replaced by 'left,' and gray if it is neither white nor black. It is easy to verify that the squares of the left column are not black and that those of the right column are not white; it is as easy to verify that black and white squares are never neighbors. It follows that gray squares, if prohibited for the king, prevent his traveling from the left to the right border of the chessboard, and hence that a rook can travel from top to bottom along the gray squares. Considering now the vertical component of PQ and calling squares white, black, or gray according as this component points up or down or both, we can find on the path of the rook a square gray in the new sense: it contains points P with PQ directed up and others with PQ directed down. It follows that it has points P' with a horizontal PQ, and, since it is gray in the former sense too, points P'' with a vertical PQ. If the square is small, such an abrupt change of direction is impossible unless the vector PQ is small itself for all P of the square. Considering a division of the board into n^2 squares, and letting n increase, we reach in the limit a point P_0 with vanishing $P_0 Q_0$—which means that the contraction does not alter the position of P_0.

(280) Proposed by S. Ulam and proved by K. Borsuk in *Fundamenta Mathematicae*, 20 (1933), pp. 177-90.

(281) L. E. J. Brouwer.

(282) The law of adiabatics is due to S. D. Poisson (1781-1840). Law of Boyle: 1662.

(284) Cf. *nn*. 28, 29.

(285) J. G. Smith and A. J. Duncan, *Sampling Statistics and Applications*, New York, McGraw-Hill, 1945, pp. 137-52.

(289) J. B. Trevan, *Proceedings of the Royal Society*, B 101 (1927), p. 483.

(290, 291, 292) A. J. Lotka, *Elements of Physical Biology*, Baltimore, Williams and Wilkins, 1925. He gives the following references: p. 70: H. G. Thornton, *Annual of Applied Biology*, 1922, p. 265; p. 74: H. S. Reed and R. H. Holland, *Proceedings of the National Academy of Sciences*, 5 (1919), p. 140; p. 360: *American Reference Book*, 1914, p. 235, *World Almanac*, 1921, p. 277, *Statistical Abstracts*, 1920, p. 814; p. 103: *Tables of Glover*. Using the works referred to above, Lotka calculated the functions; our drawings are based on his data.

(293) F. E. Croxton and D. J. Cowden, *Applied General Statistics*, New York, Prentice-Hall, 1946, ch. 16, pp. 452-58; Chart 171, p. 457. The logistic curve was discovered by the Belgian mathematician, Verhulst. Cf. Raymond Pearl, *The Biology of Population Growth*, New York, A. A. Knopf, 1925, ch. xviii.

THIS BOOK MAY BE KEPT

14 Days

and may be renewed if not called for by
someone else.
A fine of ⬤ per day is charged if the book
is kept after the last date stamped below.

DUE	DUE	DUE
DEC 17		
May 18 '59		
Warwick		
OCT 11 '61		
NOV 8 '61		
NOV 25 1961		
MAY 12 '65		